OSIAN's
swaraj for the arts

Select Masterpieces of INDIAN MODERN & CONTEMPORARY ART

Auction | 30 June 2009 | Mumbai

Select Masterpieces of

Indian Modern & Contemporary Art

Auction | 30 June 2009 | Mumbai

OSIAN's

Founder Chairman
Neville Tuli

Publishing & Design House

PUBD

The Osianama

Osian's forthcoming cultural institution at the erstwhile Minerva Cinema, will be a uniquely integrated platform from which Osian's will begin to share, on a daily basis, its vast collection and knowledge base with the public.

OSMA

- Osian's Museum
- Theatre Duplex
- Arena Argument
- Contemporary Exhibition Spaces
- Book & Design Store
- Auction House
- Appreciation & Education Courses
- Research Library & Archive

OSIAN's

creativity in infrastructure

Art Advisory Services & Art Funds

The Auction House

Established in 2000 as India's first professional Art Auction House. The wealth generated by the auction house has allowed Osian's to build a unique internally cross-subsidized cultural institutional framework.

Centre for Archiving Research & Development

- The Osian's Archive & Museum Collection
- The Library
- Digital Databank
- The Conservation Laboratory
- Research Cells

Public Interface

The Film House

- **fF.O.O.D.** The Film Fund: Osian's Originating Development
- Osian's Cinemaya
- Osian's Cinefan
- **The Film & Memorabilia Archives**

Osian's Cinefan Festival of Asian & Arab Cinema

Web World

The world of Indian, Asian & World Art, Literature & Cinema

NEW RESEARCH ENGINE TO BE LAUNCHED IN OCTOBER 2009

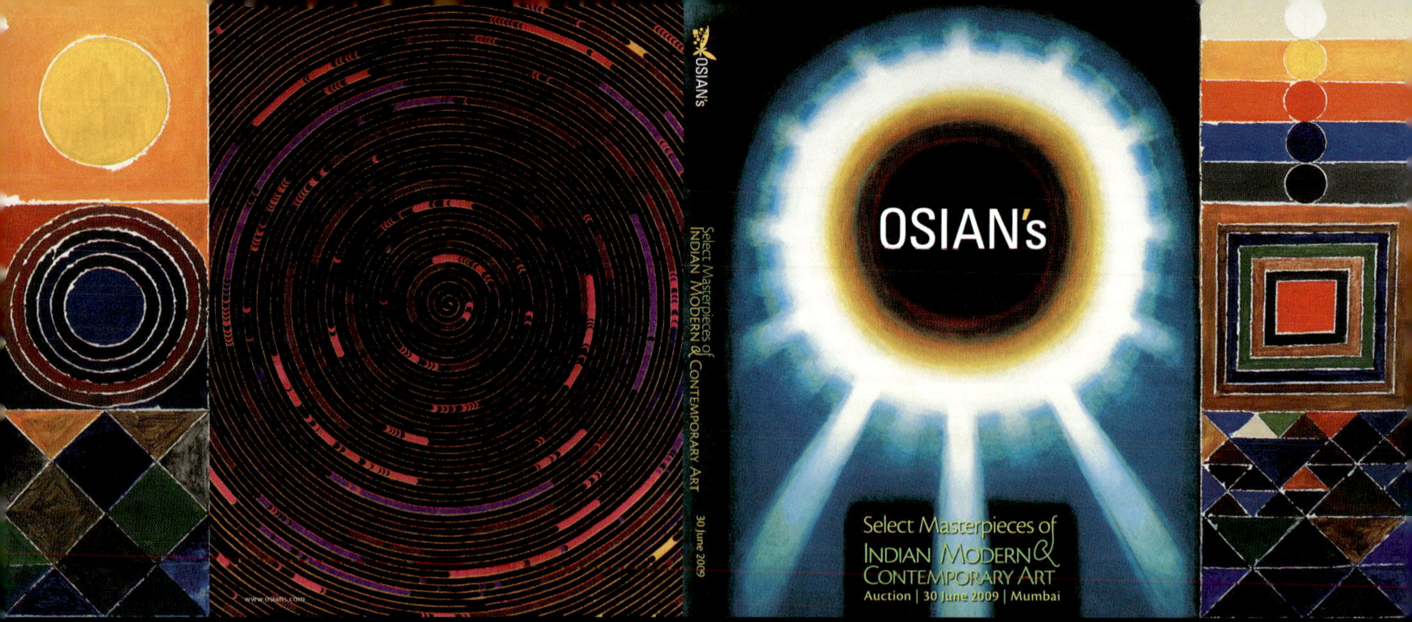

ɔSIAN'S AUCTION HOUSE, PUBLISHING AND DESIGN HOUSE
x CARD (CENTER OF ARCHIVING, RESEARCH & DEVELOPMENT)
-lead Neville Tuli

SPECIALISTS
Modern & Contemporary Art Neeti Mallick (SS),
Sheen Bhatia & Sonali Engineer
Film Memorabilia Aditi Mittal
Books & Prints Dr. Sangayya Sirurmath & Rajeshwari Shah
Prints & Photography Sucharita Apte
Crafts & Artifacts Puja Kaushik
Antiquities Rajeshwari Shah & Sucharita Apte

DESIGN HOUSE
Design & Production Team Sanjay Colaco
Vilas D'Britto & Mohammad Yakoob

DIGITAL DATABANK
Head Ashok Vaidikar
Team Chandrakant Jadhav & Kishor Vaity

LIBRARY
Head Dr. Sangayya Sirurmath
Team Ramesh Bidi & Bhojaraju Gowda

ARCHIVING & RESEARCH CELL
Akansha Rastogi (Arts); Aditi Mittal, Devdutt Trivedi, Deepti
D'Cunha & Meera Mukundan (Film); Sucharita Apte & Milind Nimse
(Prints & Photography); Rajeshwari Shah (Antiquities)

CONSERVATION LABORATORY & CATALOGUING SUPPORT
Head Sanjay Dhar
Team Lalit K. Pathak, Anant & Madhura Shelke
Amitesh Kumar, Aditya Kanth, Abdur Rasheed, Sangeeta Kumari
Gaurav Kumar, Karan S. Sachan & Sanjeet Mahalik
Murtaza Saify & Mangesh Masurkar

In conjunction with Osian's Auction
SELECT MASTERPIECES OF INDIAN MODERN
& CONTEMPORARY ART
Tuesday **30 June** 2009
The Taj Mahal Palace & Tower Apollo Bunder, Mumbai.

Produced & Published in India (June 2009)
by Osian's – Connoisseurs of Art Pvt. Ltd.

G–2B Nariman Bhavan Nariman Point, Mumbai 400 021. INDIA
T +91 22 6632 4070 **F** +91 22 6632 5655 **E** hq@osians.com

B-35 Qutub Institutional Area, New Delhi 110 016. INDIA
T +91 11 4174 3166 **F** +91 11 4174 3177 **E** newdelhi@osians.com
www.osians.com

PRINTING
JAK Printers Pvt. Ltd.
JAK Compound, Dadoji Konddeo Cross Lane
Off Dr. Babasaheb Ambedkar Marg
Byculla (East) Mumbai 400 027
T +91 22 23772222 **F** +91 22 23771212 **E** jakprint@vsnl.net

Lots for Sale 58
pp 144 & 60 + colour reproductions

ISBN 81-8174-031-9 (Osian's)

OSIAN's Presents

Select Masterpieces of Indian Modern & Contemporary Art

Opening preview

20 June 2009
at G–2B Nariman Bhavan
Nariman Point, Mumbai
7 pm onwards

Private preview

By Appointment Only
22–29 June 2009
at G–2B Nariman Bhavan
Nariman Point, Mumbai

Enquiries & information

Absentee & Telephone Bids
Neeti Mallick

Sourcing & Consignments
Sheen Bhatia
Sonali Engineer
Aditi Mittal
Sucharita Apte

Publications & Results
Supriya Chawla

Payments, Insurance & Shipping
Videsh Hate

T +91 22 6632 4070
+91 11 4174 3155
F +91 22 6632 5655
+91 11 4174 3177
E hq@osians.com

For Further Details Please Contact

Mumbai
Yasmine
T +91 22 6632 5153
F +91 22 6632 5655
E auctions@osians.com

Delhi
Taniya Malhotra
T +91 11 4174 3155
F +91 11 4174 3177
E newdelhi@osians.com

Auction

Tuesday 30 June 2009
By Invitation Only
Please be seated by 7:30pm

All Lots offered here are subject to the Terms & Conditions in this publication.

Select Masterpieces of
INDIAN MODERN &
CONTEMPORARY ART

CONTENTS

Index

J. Sultan Ali
Lot 1

Ambadas
Lot 2

K.H. Ara
Lot 3

Manjit Bawa
Lot 4

Bikash Bhattacharjee
Lot 5

Bikash Bhattacharjee
Lot 6

Avinash Chandra
Lot 7

Jogen Chowdhury
Lot 8

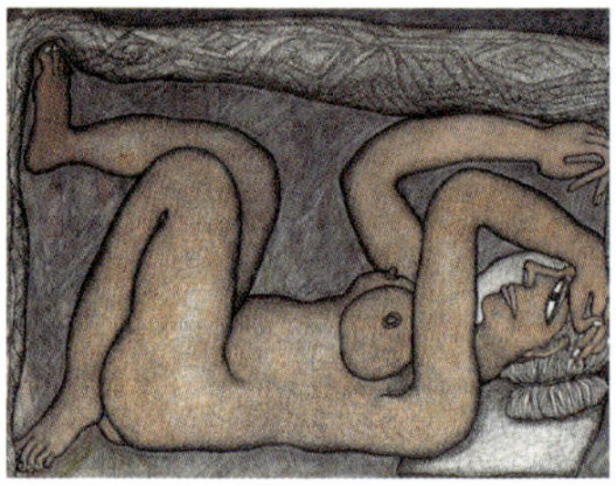

Amitava Das
Lot 9

Sunil Das
Lot 10

Biren De
Lot 11

Biren De
Lot 12

M.V. Dhurandhar
Lot 13

Anju Dodiya
Lot 14

Anju Dodiya
Lot 15

Atul Dodiya
Lot 16

Atul Dodiya
Lot 17

Select Masterpieces of INDIAN MODERN & CONTEMPORARY ART

Atul Dodiya
Lot 18

V.S. Gaitonde
Lot 19

V.S. Gaitonde
Lot 20

K. Laxma Goud
Lot 21

Satish Gujral
Lot 22

M.F. Husain
Lot 23

M.F. Husain
Lot 24

M.F. Husain
Lot 25

Krishen Khanna
Lot 26

Bharti Kher
Lot 27

Bharti Kher
Lot 28

Riyas Komu
Lot 29

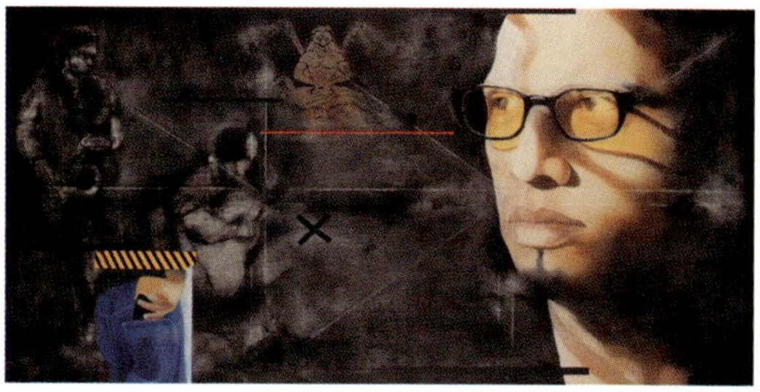

Bari Kumar
Lot 30

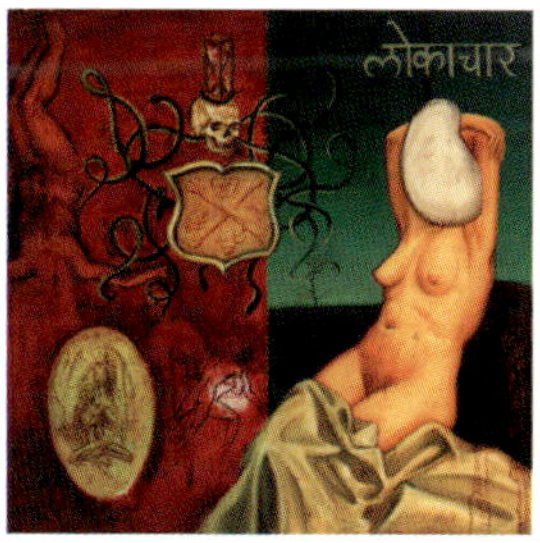

Dhruva Mistry
Lot 31

Sailoz Mookherjea
Lot 32

Index

A.H. Muller
Lot 33

L. Munuswamy
Lot 34

Shibu Natesan
Lot 35

Akbar Padamsee
Lot 36

Akbar Padamsee
Lot 37

Akbar Padamsee
Lot 38

Baiju Parthan
Lot 39

Baiju Parthan
Lot 40

Ganesh Pyne
Lot 41

Ganesh Pyne
Lot 42

A. Ramachandran
Lot 43

V. Ramesh
Lot 44

Ramkumar
Lot 45

Ramkumar
Lot 46

Ramkumar
Lot 47

S.H. Raza
Lot 48

Select Masterpieces of Indian Modern & Contemporary Art

S.H. Raza
Lot 49

Jamini Roy
Lot 50

Jamini Roy
Lot 51

Sadequain
Lot 52

Sadequain
Lot 53

G.R. Santosh
Lot 54

Himmat Shah
Lot 55

Nataraj Sharma
Lot 56

F.N. Souza
Lot 57

F.N. Souza
Lot 58

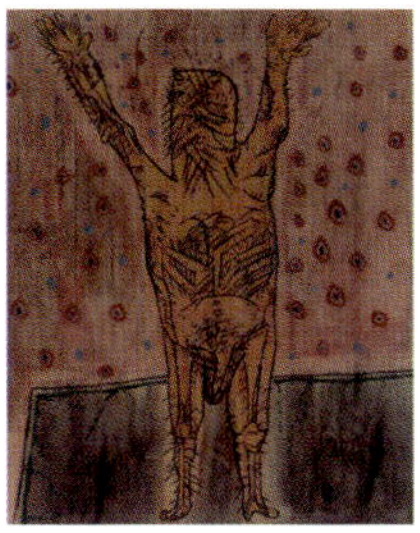

1

J. Sultan Ali

(1920 – 1990)

Kammu Katta

Oil on canvas, 1973
Signed in Devanagari 'Ali' and S/d in English 'Sultan Ali 1973' l.r.
31.2 x 53.2 in (79.4 x 134.8 cm)

Inscribed in English 'J. SULTAN ALI, KAMMU. KATTA, 79 x 135 cms. (31" x 53") OIL ON CANVAS, 1973.' on verso

INR 1,600,000 – 2,000,000
USD 33,330 – 41,670

In Sultan Ali's mature works inspiration comes directly from the chastity of forms in tribal art. His predilection has been to intersperse nature and its relationship with man in a system of codes/ symbols that he uses and re-uses. He revisits 'the given' – the religion, the mythic world of gods and goddesses, re-structuring and personalizing the systems of signs and symbols. The characters in his works are derivations of earthen gods such as *nagadevatas, bhoodevi* (earth goddess), fire, water, sun-god, and his canvas becomes the stage where forces of nature freeze as pictorial notations, lending humour to his works. Profound themes and thoughts such as victory of good over evil, peace are communicated playfully. The detailed drawings show his draftsmanship. The text becomes analogous to the entire composition, and acts as a decorative element crucial to the picture-space contributing in the relative positioning of the main figure. Thus in Sultan Ali's world bird, beast, bull, snake, owl, man are brought together in an intimate relationship.

2

Ambadas

(b.1922)

Commotion Crystalised series

Oil on canvas, 1964
35.1 x 35.2 in (89.0 x 89.2 cm)

Condition

Previously restored, stable cracks present. Loss of paint on t.l. corner.

INR 1,000,000 – 1,250,000
USD 20,830 – 26,040

" Art to me is a happening and performance – an instant plunging, flirting and merging with life with being and becoming. All that is there on the canvas is but a celebration... The feeling of unlimitedness envelopes – something mystical in a sense. Like a dancer who performs not for herself but for the spectator. The dancer becomes the spectator and the dance... later as a painter, I became aware of everything: nature, moving innately and rising towards its optimal expression. This phenomenon, which comprises the infinite order of the cosmic whole, was an inspiration to me as it burst upon me. It motivated my experiences and understanding of art... Most art, whether classical, academic or traditional remain bound up to a dualistic notion, reducing itself to a myth of subject and object. The real escapes, for it is seen as flux, without order... For a number of artists, the main preoccupation is to get past the surface reality into 'the Real' which is pure and formless." Ambadas, November 1996; reprinted in *Chemould* ExC. 1998.

3

K.H. Ara
(1913 – 1985)

Woman and Desire
Gouache on paper pasted on cardboard, 1933
S/d in English 'ARA 1933' l.r.
37.2 x 16.4 in (94.5 x 41.7 cm)

INR 2,400,000 – 3,000,000
USD 50,000 – 62,500

Ara improvises on the symbolism of "primordial sin" in Christian mythology – the scene of temptation, Satan tempts Eve to eat the forbidden fruit from the Tree of Knowledge that leads to the fall of Man. He uses "the familiar" image of serpent and half-naked woman in the wilderness.

Lot 3 is one of the rare early works of the 1930s in Ara's oeuvre, amidst his famous nudes and still-life studies.

4

Manjit Bawa
(1914 – 2008)

Untitled
Oil on canvas, 2006
S/d in English 'Manjit Bawa 06'
on verso
90.0 x 65.7 in (228.6 x 166.7 cm)

INR 8,000,000 – 10,000,000
USD 166,670 – 208,330

"The deeply reflective mode in some of his [Manjit Bawa] iconic images have to do with the notion of *zikr* or remembrance in *sama* or the act of listening as practiced by the Sufis traveling through and experiencing the vastness of ecology...It could be argued that Manjit's work in his last phase has moved assuredly away from a typological iconography of the face. There is an unambiguous aspiration towards emblematic remembrance. This is the way of approaching the domain of subjectivity, perhaps." – Madan Gopal Singh, rpt. in *Bhav, Bhaav, Bhavya*, Sakshi Gallery, Mumbai/ Impresario, Calcutta/ Gallery Espace, New Delhi, 1999, pp. 27-8, ExC.

5

Bikash Bhattacharjee

(1940 –2006)

And the Twilight

Oil on canvas, 1979
S/d in English 'Bikash 79' l.r.
41.1 x 47.0 in (104.3 x 119.4 cm)

Inscribed in English " - AND THE TWILIGHT' / BIKASH BHATTACHARJEE / 2D NABO KUMAR RAHA LANE, CALCUTTA -700004 / INDIA' on verso

INR 3,600,000 – 4,500,000
USD 75,000 – 93,750

Illustrated Reference

Close To Events: Works of Bikash Bhattacharjee
Manasij Majumder, Niyogi Books, 2007, p166-167, Full Colour plate.

"*Twilight* is a rooftop view of old Calcutta recalling Bikash's 1964 *Spring at the Roof Top*. The cityscape here is equally drab but not as in the latter gleaming in the morning sun of early spring. Instead, dusking in the fading light after sundown it symbolically backdrops a neatly dressed poor middle class woman in the twilight of her youth, left to herself in her free time on the rooftop terrace listening to music on her transistor set, her only pastime. She is unmarried and ageing, with little charm left in her looks to attract any male gaze from the rooftops of the neighboring houses, which in her unseeing eyes appear lifeless and empty. Not only her blank eyes but the whole face bears the scars of repression of a young woman growing old to be a lonely spinster in an indigent conservative family. The tonalities of colours evoking the subdued evening light cast a splendid spell of pathos all over the canvas." – Manasij Majumder, **Close To Events: Works of Bikash Bhattacharjee**, Niyogi Books, 2007, p156.

6

Bikash Bhattacharjee
(1940 –2006)

Prostitute series
Oil on canvas, 1987
Signed in English 'BIKASH' l.r.
41.7 x 39.7 in (106.0 x 101.0 cm)

INR 3,600,000 – 4,500,000
USD 75,000 – 93,750

"Most of the female presences in Bhattacharjee's painting exude various shades of sensuality... Whereas the married woman is idealised as a mother, direct sexuality belongs to regions far from home. It is observed in the self-deceptive aberrations resulting from misused freedom of affluent girls or in women of red light areas. The latter are treated with understanding, closeness and compassion. The artist pities them knowing that their condition was not willingly chosen. Hence, he strives to reveal their humaneness upheld despite the profession or even through it...The ordinary, often vulgar fact of prostitutes waiting for customers becomes symbolic of forlorn women's yearning for love...The prostitute as a human being, used and left behind, yet, giving herself – heart and body – stands for our expectation of loving response and turns into a symbol of women as such." – Marta Jakimowicz-Karle, rpt. in **Bikash Bhattacharjee**, Kala Yatra, 1991, p35.

7

Avinash Chandra

(1931 – 1991)

New York

Acrylic on canvas, 1969
S/d in English 'Avinash 69' l.l. and on verso
48.1 x 60.2 in (122.2 x 153.0 cm)

INR 3,600,000 – 4,500,000
USD 75,000 – 93,750

"There is an ambiguity to all of his imagery that can be understood through a layering of psychological import: at first glance they are one thing and on closer inspection, or at a different glance they are something else. They are often at once structures and figures, full of energy and static, anthropomorphic and human... His are 'symbolic presences', however a personal symbolism that is open and non-particular – generic shapes of people in landscape, sun, moon, building... In 1967 Chandra won a Fairfield Foundation Fellowship for Travel and Study to New York, and although he was exhibiting and selling regularly in the United States he returned to London in 1973." – Dr. Rachel Garfield, rpt. in **Avinash Chandra: A Retrospective**, Osborne Samuel LLP, Berkley Square Gallery, London, 2006, p12.

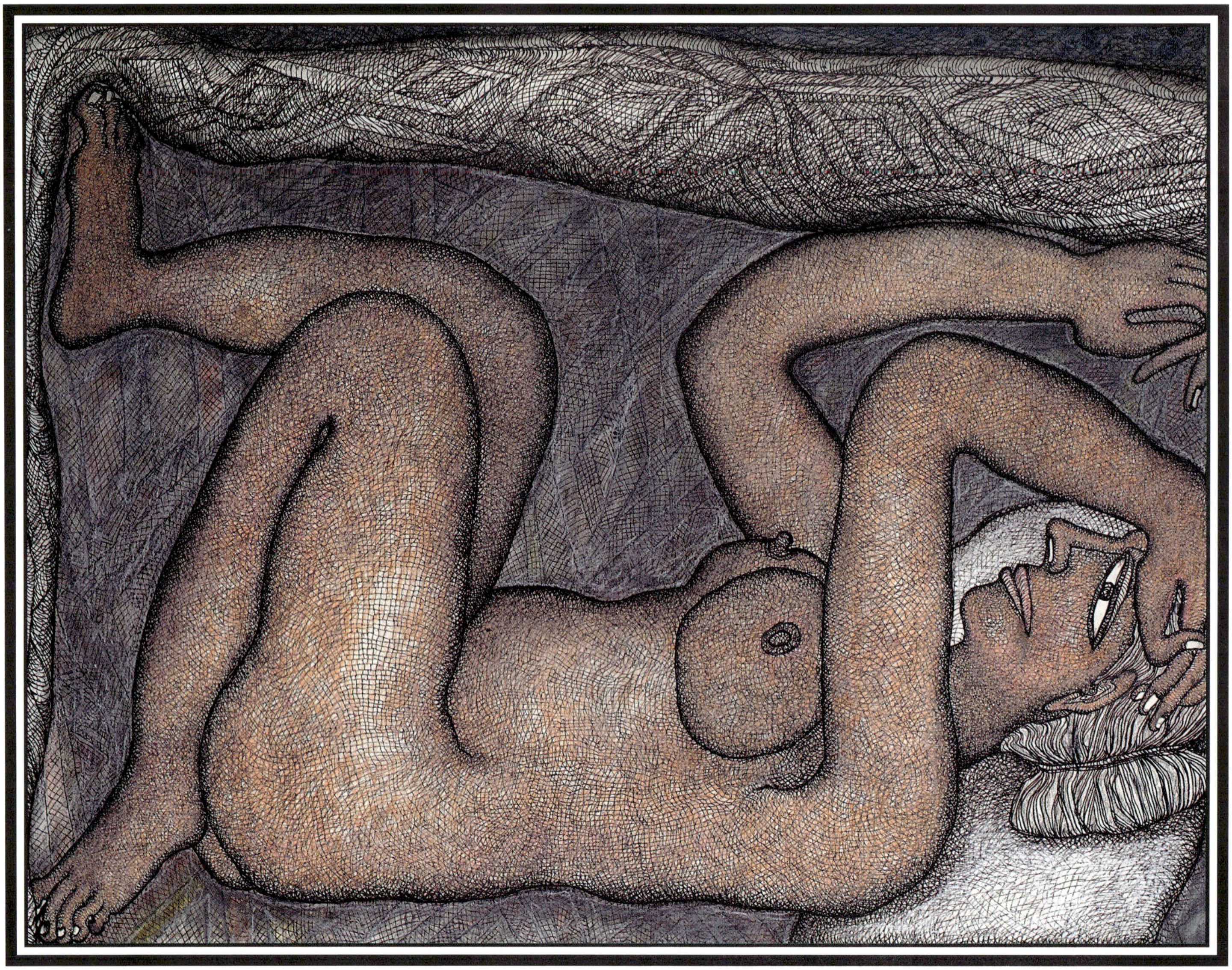

8

Jogen Chowdhury

(b.1939)

Woman under the quilt

Pen & ink and pastel on paper pasted on board, 2004
22.1 x 28.0 in (56.0 x 71.2 cm)

Inscribed in English 'Artist: Jogen Chowdhury, Title: "Woman under the quilt (2004)", Size: 56.2 x 71.2 cm, Medium: Pen & Ink and Pastles, Year: 2004' on verso

INR 4,000,000 – 5,000,000
USD 83,330 – 104,170

Lot 8 shows a nude on bed under the quilt. She is lost in her reverie. This work at once reminds one of Ismat Chughtai's short story '*Lihaaf*'. The viewer is made a party to this voyeuristic pleasure.

"Jogen's images are both new and magical because they are radically transformed. There is a nerve ending here, a bite and tension to these paintings...This tension, as much as the fascinating mix of the finite and the fantastic, is basic to the genre of Jogen's work. In the later portraits, an edge is brought to the pictures with satire that responds to his growing indictment of society."

9

Amitava Das
(b.1947)

The eyes that will not look....'
Oil and acrylic on canvas, 1999
61.6 x 55.4 in (156.7 x 140.7 cm)

S/d in English 'Amitava Das 99' on verso

INR 1,200,000 – 1,500,000
USD 25,000 – 31,250

Illustration Reference
Amitava Das... The Outsider, Sakshi Gallery, ExC, Mumbai, February 2000

"I innovated another technique of drawing - drawing by elimination. I covered the printed surface with linear forms and shapes. Later on, I would eliminate them by applying the strokes of pen, and slowly it would get covered with the blackness of the ink. The images were very introvert at that time. The treatment of the space was suggestive of interiors (architecture). This process reminds me of the 17th century canvas painting by Rembrandt who worked, not on a white canvas but on a dark canvas. He would eliminate the dark areas with the light areas...I don't see my drawings as a preparatory study in the conventional sense, but as complete works of art. I would like to term them works on paper, not mere drawing or water colour. Like you break silence by a musical note."
– Amitava Das, rpt. in **Amitava: Works on Paper From 1972 to 1994,** ExC, Sakshi Gallery.

10

Sunil Das
(b.1939)

Woman series
Oil on canvas, 1999
S/d in English 'Sunil 99' t.r.
55.6 x 55.6 in (140.8 x 140.8 cm)

Inscribed in English 'Sunil DAS, Calcutta 464-0971' on verso

INR 1,200,000 – 1,500,000
USD 25,000 – 31,250

"Passing years found me yielding more and more of my worked-in surface to the phenomenon of woman. The beholder of my work was to discover that my gaze was not transfixed on the rich contours of the female form only. The curves and the cleavages, the concaves and convexes, the narrowings and the broadenings, the projections and recessions of the female anatomy have increasingly made me curious about the unseen, and therefore, mysterious aspects of womanhood. Baring of the female body which for ages engaged male artists' art practice has become less meaningful to me. Even otherwise unraveling of the mystery of womanhood has no meaning for me. I would rather let my women remain unfathomable in their shrouded mystery. I would be happy if my women send enigmatic signals with their gazes, twist of neck, turns of head and make signs with their hands and fingers to indicate states of their minds and desire of their souls." – Sunil Das, rpt. in 'My Woman', **Sunil Das In Retrospect 1957–2003**, ExC, 2003, ITC Hotel, Kolkata

11

Biren De

(b.1926)

The Moment

Oil on canvas, 1967
S/d in English 'Biren de 67' l.l.
53 x 42.1 in (134.6 x 107.0 cm)

Inscribed in English 'THE MOMENT-May 67. BIREN DE' on verso

Condition

Minor paint loss c.l., stable cracks at some places

INR 2,400,000 – 3,000,000
USD 50,000 – 62,500

'These symbols or shapes which are mainly erotic – are in fact shorn of eroticism, they are almost scientific hieroglyphs. Painted on a monumental scale they fill the space with their brooding presence.Texture is mostly abandoned for a smoky application of colour. The colour is vibrant and rich with large areas of black or 'dark' and with occasional areas of purple or green. The sensuousness of the subject is reduced to a kind of solid torpor, the great principles of Yin and Yang become some strange resonant diagram that seems to beat with the pulse beat of the earth. Biren's recent work seeks the unity of these and other fundamental shapes.' - Jaya Appaswamy rpt. in *Biren De as seen by 5 contemporaries* 1972 rpt. from LKC 1967.

12

Biren De

(b.1926)

Untitled

Oil on canvas, 1974
S/d in English 'Biren de 74' l.l. and on verso
55.1 x 40.0 in (140.0 x 101.6 cm)

Inscribed in English 'APRIL 74 (b), BIREN DE' on verso. Label of 'Hamish Dewar Ltd, Conservation and Restoration of Paintings' on the middle bar of the stretcher

INR 2,400,000 – 3,000,000
USD 50,000 – 62,500

"The composite 'whole', mandala, result of conglomeration of subsidiary energies, and held together by the 'diamond-core', the bindu, has a white-hot aura all around. The psyche travels continuously towards this aural rim, touches it, then comes back invariably to the core again, thus giving the whole experience a simultaneous outward-inward thrust. Then, slowly, and in keeping with the pace of one's transcendental evolution, this composite ball of energy with its ever-expanding aura, starts its journey, thereby causing rupture of planes around it. Gradually, this continuing process of psychic experience takes one beyond all sensations of the phenomenal world, bringing him nearer and nearer to an efflorescence, as it were, of expanded consciousness. So the fixed central point – the still centre – within our being, therefore, is the initiator of all our movements as well as the home, the ultimate reality, to which we return." – Ajit Mookerjee, rpt. in **Biren De**, LKA, 1985.

13

M.V. DHURANDHAR

(1867 – 1944)

Battle Scene from the Mahabharata

Oil on canvas pasted on board, 1922
37.2 x 25.2 in (94.5 x 64.2 cm)

S/d in English 'Dhurandhar 5.1922' l.l.

Provenance

Previously from the Collection of H.H. The Maharawal Shri Virendrasinghiji Chauhan Raja of Chhota Udaipur State

INR 1,600,000 – 2,000,000
USD 33,333 – 41,667

14

Anju Dodiya

(b.1964)

Blessing

Watercolour, charcoal & pastel on paper, 2003
Signed in English 'anju' on verso
44.7 x 44.7 in (113.5 x 113.5 cm)

Inscribed in English 'ANJU DODIYA 2003, WATERCOLOUR, CHARCOAL & SOFT PASTEL ON PAPER 44 1/2" x 45" Title 'BLESSING" on verso

Condition

Previously restored

INR 1,600,000 – 2,000,000
USD 33,330 – 41,670

Anju Dodiya's expressions can be expressed as autobiographical. In Anju's own words this lot is a portrayal of "an arm descending from the clouds... a loom of fruit appearing through the haze. Was thinking of the murals of Pompeii and a glimpse of an image, a colour, amidst ruins".

15

Anju Dodiya
(b.1964)

Coronation II
Acrylic on velvet mattress, 2004
Signed in English 'anju dodiya' on verso
48.1 x 46.0 x 7.3 in (214.5 x 116.8 x 18.5 cm)

Inscribed in English 'ANJU DODIYA 2004,
Title: CORONATION II' on verso

INR 4,000,000 – 5,000,000
USD 83,330 – 104,170

Exhibition Reference
'After Dark', Cu. Gayatri Sinha, Sakshi Gallery, Mumbai, 2004

As against the stringent two-dimensionality of the canvas, Anju Dodiya for the very first time indulged into creating textured patterns on mattresses for the Hyatt Hotels on the theme of 'Shiva Parvati Marriage'. Her second innings with the three-dimensional velvet mattress began with the Gayatri Sinha curated show titled 'After Dark'. The above lot is one of the three works done on velvet mattress that was part of the exhibition. The mattress is used as a metaphor to express her concerns about an artist's inner life which is full of doubts and anxiety leading to insomnia. 'Coronation II' is about self mockery where the artist has tried placing an emphasis on the slowing down of the creative mind because of the fundamental darkness within, represented in the form of a medieval weapon, tribulus (caltrop) which serves the purpose of a speed breaker, slowing down the advance.

अतुल
ATUL

16

Atul Dodiya
(b.1959)

Destination
Oil & bee's wax on canvas, 1984
S/d in English 'ATUL 84' on verso
50.2 x 59.4 in (127.5 x 152.1 cm)

INR 2,400,000 – 3,000,000
USD 50,000 – 62,500

Inspired by American neo-Dadaist realist Jasper Johns 'Targets' and Pop & Commercial Art, the spiritual and the abstract as text and image both together became a distinct style of Atul Dodiya's in the mid 80s. Torn posters, graffitti on the wall, advertisements, all added to his thought process. He created some four – five paintings with a focus on targets. On the similar line to Johns, this painting of Dodiya's features a depiction of an actual target. A closer view reveals black holes on the surface of the canvas. The mind useful in its own way adjusts itself in different ways to anything. The concentric bands can be elaborated to figure distraction rather than focus. The compass used to create the optical bands ultimately ends up producing the image of the 'target'. This is the only period where he (Atul) uses his first name to create a painterly statement right in the middle of the artwork with an emphasis on the letter 'T' in Devnāgari distinctly seperating it with the use of black colour.

17

Atul Dodiya

(b.1959)

As Though He Listened

Oil on canvas, 1987
Signed in English 'Atul' on verso
60.1 x 63.9 in (152.2 x 162.4 cm)

Inscribed in English 'ATUL B DODIYA, 'AS THOUGH HE LISTENED, 1987, 153 cm x 163 cm' on verso

INR 8,000,000 – 10,000,000
USD 166,670 – 208,330

Refer to Lot 77 in Exhibition-Auction 'The Intuitive-Logic II', Cu. Neville Tuli, HEART, 1997, titled 'Man in the Gallery' (1985) which is a set of 3 paper works, depicting a man with a collar band viewing an artwork (A Bust) placed on a pedestal. The above work Lot 17 is in continuum, the man with a collar band is in conversation with an artist (perhaps). The wall foregrounds the two men in conversation and an artobject placed on a pedestal for viewing. Humour in the entire episode is noteworthy – the expression on the face of the Bust (artwork), who coincidentally resembles the man wearing a collar band, and the tilted plant. The Gallery opens to the road / the outside world. Fun in everyday things, the ordinariness of the visual is where Atul's humour works best.

"Dodiya's world is self-confident. He presents his characters without irony, nostalgia or rage. He is not defensive about their social status, which is that of the comfortable middle class. There is no apology in these works or anything. We see the exactness with which a figure is stationed at a certain point, the meticulousness of one tone of colour against another, the almost finicky measuring of distances between objects. All these function as reverberating foci against each other." – Gieve Patel, rpt. in 'Atul Dodiya', Gallery Chemould, ExC, 1989.

18

ATUL DODIYA

(b.1959)

Roadside with Temple

Oil on canvas, 1988
Signed in English 'ATUL' on verso
46.9 x 71.1 in (119.4 x 180.8 cm)

Inscribed in English 'ATUL DODIYA, ROADSIDE WITH TEMPLE, 122CM x 181CM, OIL, 1988' on verso

Condition

Preservation work has been carried out in 2009 by Osian's Conservation Department, Mumbai

INR 6,400,000 – 8,000,000
USD 133,330 – 166,670

Exhibition Reference

'Atul Dodiya', Gallery Chemould, Bombay, 1989

This work is from his (Atul Dodiya's) first solo exhibition of nine oil paintings held in 1989 at Gallery Chemould, Bombay. Largely inspired by David Hockney, his works primarily are rendered in the photo-realistic mode. It was in the late 1980s when Atul formally started experimenting with the landscapes of semi-urban India. Says Dodiya "Realism has always been more recognizable". With the power of pure colour and form Dodiya has proved that a monumental picturesque is a process of seeing and thinking. Atul Dodiya has autographed the canvas with the first two letters of his name, which appear as a signboard in the distance. The view on the canvas is from a street in Gondal (a small town near Rajkot, Gujarat) and also the artist's hometown.

"The single most compelling thing in Atul Dodiya's recent work is the degree of tension held within each painting. The exhibition comes across to the viewer as something of a force...Having touched the work at some of its core, one may now sit back to enjoy the rich variety in the depiction. The visual wit which shows only the tip of a red hydrant reflected in a grey monsoon puddle; or the colourful drips on the sides of a canvas-in-the-making...The unity of tension identifies them as belonging to the inner world of one artist, erupting from out the richness of an empty room."
– Gieve Patel, rpt. in **Atul Dodiya**, ExC, Gallery Chemould, 1989.

19

V.S. GAITONDE

(1924 – 2001)

Untitled

Oil on canvas, 1969
S/d in Devanagari and English
'GAITONDE 69' on verso
35.1 x 30.1 in (89.2 x 76.5 cm)

INR 16,000,000 – 20,000,000
USD 333,330 – 416,670

Illustrated Reference

Painting from the same series is illustrated in full colour in N. Tuli's *The Flamed – Mosaic : Indian Contemporary Painting*. New Delhi : HEART and Mapin Publishing 1997. Plate 160, p.222.

" Gaitonde's explorations regarding the luminosities and densities of colour, could best be clarified if one tries to imagine the formation of puddles of water on a marble floor, hand in hand with their consequent drying process. Random shapes emerge, only to disappear and re-emerge. These uncertainties are played with, each moment demanding a stillness. Soon one feels that randomness has been given sufficient freedom, and is about to return the compliment, revealing herself through some recognisable form". – Neville Tuli, *ibid*, p.258.

20

V.S. Gaitonde
(1924 – 2001)

Untitled
Oil on canvas, 1972
S/d in Devanagari & English
'Gaitonde 72' on verso
54.9 x 40.3 in (139.5 x 102.2 cm)

Provenance
Private Collection, Mumbai

INR 24,000,000 – 30,000,000
USD 500,000 – 625,000

Illustrated Reference
Painting from the same series is illustrated in *The Flamed – Mosaic : Indian Contemporary Painting*. New Delhi : HEART and Mapin Publishing 1997. Plate 8, pp.33

"Texture is structure. How he achieves this texture is the secret of Gaitonde's style... In the application of the colour itself there is an order... The colour settles and congeals into a series of approximate horizontals throwing the compositional weight somewhat lower than centre and balancing the left and right of the canvas like the arms of a sccale. The order is almost deliberately obscured by the distribution of near–random forms across the surface. These topographical or hieroglyphic forms themselves are made to dissolve into the field like enamel in an encaustic."
— Pria Karunakar, LKC 19–20 (Apr–Sep 1975)

"The whole composition is more or less one colour in which the gentle gradations form a liquid matrix in which small and more solid outcrops of form appear to float. The style itself is reticent saying or suggesting only the least that needs to be stated. The colours too are limited and quiet and often consist of hues of the same colour. The whole painting has certain expansiveness because the composition is open and can be thought of as part of a larger reality. There is a certain sense of mystery in these paintings, they affect the feelings of the spectator."
— Jaya Appasamy, rpt. in 'The Paths of Abstraction', *LKC 19 &20*, April-September 1975. p.6.

21

K. Laxma Goud

(b.1940)

Untitled

Bronze, 2007
Threshold Gallery label bearing the gallery address, artist's name, medium, size and Ref. No.
33.4 x 41.1 in (84.7 x 104.4 cm)

INR 1,000,000 – 1,250,000
USD 20,830 – 26,040

Laxma Goud's works follow a nostalgic stream, wherein the duality of village life and urban existence are always in conflict. He often uses "modern guise of recycling, he constructs reassembled people – stitched, clamped, and pinned together from previously extant elements" (quoting Susan S. Bean from **Contemporary Indian Art: Other Realities** p52). In this series of bronzes, Goud focuses on the iconic image of yakshis or mother goddesses as depicted in the ancient sculptures with ornamental head gears. And the re-assembled attempt is visible in appliqué technique used in making of the work. It also reminds of K. G. Subramanyan's murals.

57

22

Satish Gujral

(b.1925)

Portrait of Jawaharlal Nehru

Oil on board, 1957
Signed in Devanagari and dated in English 'Gujral 57' t.l.
47.3 x 32.6 in (119.8 x 82.6 cm)

S/d in English 'Satish gujral 57' on verso.

Provenance

Previously from the Artist's Family Collection

INR 4,800,000 – 6,000,000
USD 100,000 – 125,000

"As the first Prime Minister of Independent India, Jawaharlal Nehru had no time to spare for activities other than political. But seeing Satish Gujral's deft hand at painting, he expressed his desire to have his portrait made by him. Satish went to Teen Murti Bhawan where, when he saw Indira Gandhi, he found her more interesting as a portrait subject than her father. He dared to express his desire to her, and a pleasantly surprised Indira shyly started giving sittings after informing her father... Nehru gave him sittings for over a month for his portrait... And Nehru's portrait in a pensive mood (1957) forms a historical part of the retrospective exhibition of Satish Gujral's paintings, paper collages and sculptures at the National Gallery of Modern Art." - Rana Siddiqui, The Hindu, Feb 6, 2006.

23

M.F. HUSAIN
(b.1915)

Untitled
Graphite and coloured pencil on
brown paper, 1941
S/d in English 'Husain 41' l.r.
21.9 x 28.9 in (55.5 x 73.5 cm)

Condition
Previously restored

INR 1,200,000 – 1,500,000
USD 25,000 – 31,250

Lot 23 represents a very rare drawing by M F Husain's from one of his earliest period when he was designing furniture for the bedroom of a child from a royal family.

24

M.F. Husain

(b.1915)

Untitled

Oil on canvas, early 1960s
Signed in English 'Husain' l.l.
19.2 x 23.5 in (48.8 x 59.7 cm)

Condition

Stable, drying cracks present

INR 4,000,000 – 5,000,000
USD 83,330 – 104,170

25

M.F. Husain
(b.1915)

Untitled
Oil on canvas, 1970
S/d in Devanagari 'Husain 70' t.r.
19.1 x 34.3 in (48.4 x 87.0 cm)

INR 3,600,000 – 4,500,000
USD 75,000 – 93,750

26

Krishen Khanna
(b.1925)

Christ
Oil on canvas, 1954
S/d in English 'K Khanna, DEC 54' on verso
22.5 x 13.2 in (57.2 x 33.4 cm)

Inscribed in English 'No 4' on verso

Condition
Stable cracks present

INR 2,400,000 – 3,000,000
USD 50,000 – 62,500

27

Bharti Kher

(b.1969)

Imposter

Fibre Glass and fur, 2004
45.1 x 36.2 x 29.9 in (114.5 x 92.2 x 76.0 cm)

INR 4,800,000 – 6,000,000
USD 100,000 – 125,000

Illustrated Reference

Bharti Kher, ExC, GallerySke and Nature Morte, 2006, p30-31

Bharti Kher's works often employ images of hybrid beings (part-human and part-animal) caught up in familiar humane environment, engaged in chores, few in domestic spaces like Arione serving chocolate muffins, Arione's sister just back from shopping, or a Family Portrait with a wolf-headed vacuum cleaner; or animals straight away enacting the human role like a giraffe committing suicide. There are traits of things gone awry, the normalcy code being broken or ignored. This encroaching violence and pervading animalism acquires a subtle expression in Lot 27 . The ape wearing jewels and fur coat act as caricatures of human indulgences and dogmas. 'Imposter' anticipates her other works where she uses the image of 'ape' such as 'The Wise One' (2006)

28

Bharti Kher

(b.1969)

Seeing Some Things Better

Mixed media on board, 2004
S/d in English 'Bharti Kher 2004' on verso
48.2 x 47.9 in (122.5 x 121.8 cm)

Titled 'Seeing some Things better' on verso

INR 4,000,000 – 5,000,000
USD 83,330 – 104,170

"Kher plays on the role of the bindi in contemporary art. Mass-produced stick-on bindis are the low-brow versions of the Bindu with a capital B, a conceptually loaded aesthetic and spatial device, valorized and self-Orientalized by modern Indian artists and architects. Kher's use of pedestrian bindis is an intellectual and cultural inversion of the mythology of the modern Bindu. By repeating the bindi endlessly and using it in subversive ways of cover surfaces that range from rexine carpets and broken cups to fiberglass animals and hybrids, Kher punctures the transcendent symbolism of the hallowed Bindu. Kher's bindi compositions make visible the dialectic of desire and consummation."
– Kanu Kartik Agarwal, rpt. in **Bharti Kher**, ExC, GallerySke and Nature Morte, 2006, p10.

29

RIYAS KOMU

(b.1971)

Pouch – full of stories (I carry weapon of your name)

Oil, acrylic and marble grain on canvas, 2002
S/d in English 'Riyas KOMU 2002' on verso
47.9 x 96.0 in (121.5 x 243.8 cm)

Inscribed in English 'POUCH - FULL OF STORIES (I CARRY WEAPON OF YOUR NAME), OIL, ACRYLIC, MARBLE GRAIN ON CANVAS, 8" x 4", 2002' on verso

INR 2,400,000 – 3,000,000
USD 50,000 – 62,500

In this work, Riyas dedicates himself in creating a larger than life size portrait of his beloved friend late Girish Dahiwale. "This work was done with the spirit of remembering the memorable days at J.J. with Girish Dahiwale" says Riyas Komu.

"Girish came to the Birla Academy to meet me recommended by Akbar Padamsee. His handsome face with long straggly tresses and a gay lissome physique belied a shy, soft-spoken, sensitive individual. Over the months (perhaps beginning from September 1997) that we met regularly, either at the gallery or our respective residences, we discussed our own premises of art and his exhibition – Toxic Tales (therapy) that happened at Birla Academy in February 1998. Eight large monochromatic larger than life self-portraits with striking meditative images with equally startling messages and titles comprised the exhibition that can be, undoubtedly, considered a signpost leading to the kind of work that has happened in the past decade. There was an inimitable overlap of the modern and the hyper-realist in Girish Dahiwale's work. Poster-like and accompanied with text the works expressed an anguish and rebel that afflicts all youth". – Niyatee Shinde

An exhibition titled 'Debt' was conceived by a band of like minded people Anant Joshi, Riyas Komu, Justin Ponmany & T.V. Santhosh in 1999 at The Guild Gallery, Mumbai in fond memories of the late Girish Dahiwale who in his own way, as a friend, as an artist, inspired each of them. This in a way was also an expression of these artists dedication towards him (Girish Dahiwale), who committed suicide at the age of 25 in 1998. Girish was among the first few artists who created paintings from photographs. Atul Dodiya paying his tribute to this youthful artist *In Five Drips from Vesuvius*, creates an image of Dahiwale (drawn from a photograph of the artist bending forward towards the huge bell as though listening to the echoes and sounds originating from the bell with bunches of grapes all strewn around). This 1998 work of Dodiya was lettered across with names of illnesses projecting a cryptogram on a large space defining life's passionate association disassociation within and without.

"'Debt' was also an emotional expression of togetherness, i.e. the times spent with Girish Dahiwale" – Justin Ponmany

"I knew him (Girish Dahiwale) through the stories his close friends used to tell me. Those were intense accounts about someone who passionately confronted the reality; raised questions against the kind of discrimination existing in the art world and laughed at follies of this material world. And then I knew him, as an example of innocence and commitment in this age of opportunistic pragmatism, who dared to sacrifice his life for romantic notions of love. I knew him as one who carried the fire of rebellion in his heart; his works reflected its sparks. He, at that young age made a mark in the history of Indian contemporary art. If he were alive now he would have stood tall as an eye opener, as he had the ambition and insight to become one. In the late 90s he came up with a language quite refreshing and showed a sense of 'coherent' experimentation in relation to execution of his ideas. His works combined elements of political poster making and advertising to address social issues at times in the pretext of personal symbolism. By extending the idea of painting into spectacular scale of 35 mm. movie screen and recurring images of his self-portraits as if in a moment of personal angst, seem to be bathed in Mumbai streetlights, give voice to the spirits of his time." – T. V. Santhosh

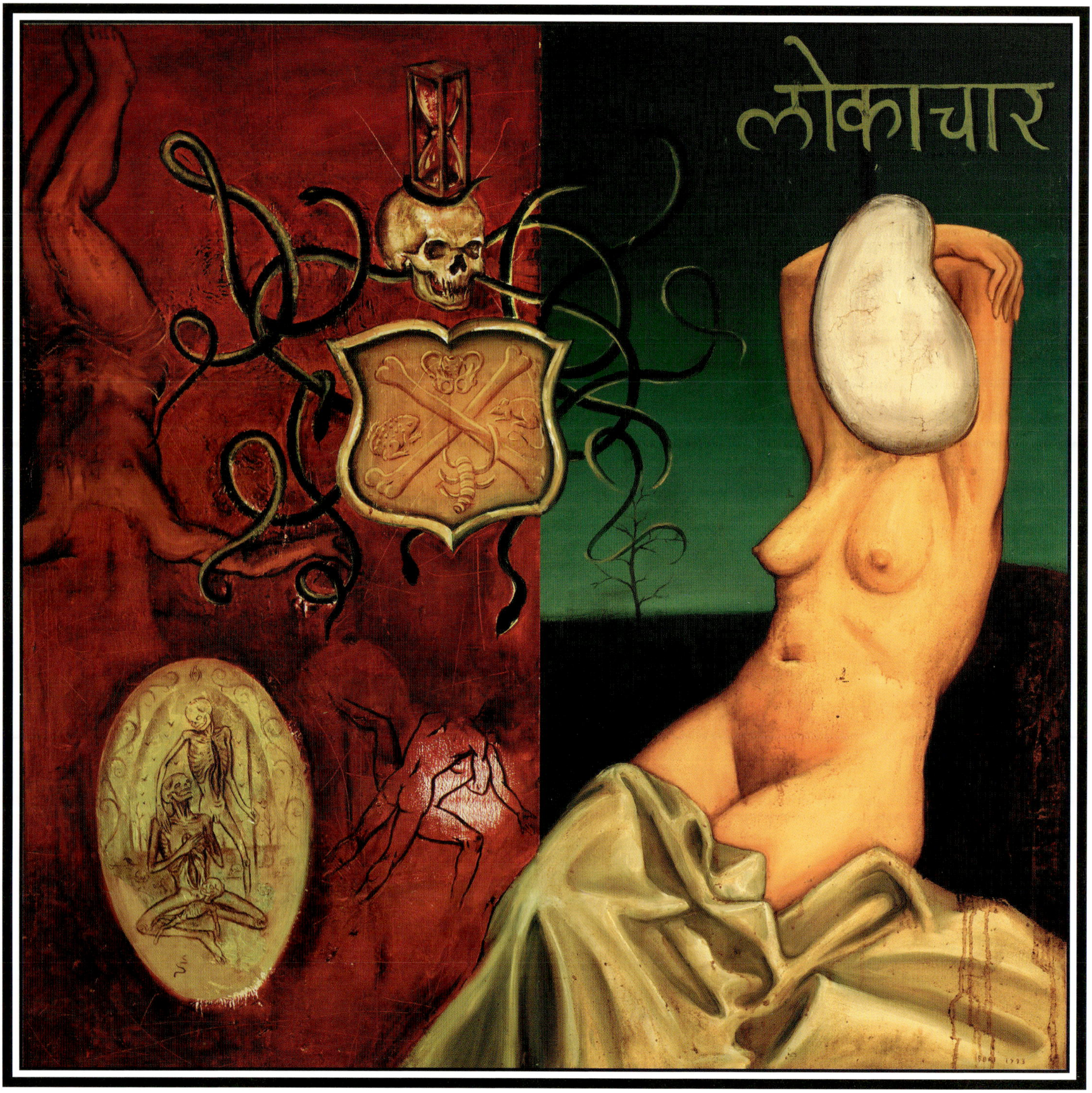

30

Bari Kumar
(b.1966)

Lokachar (Diptych)
Oil on canvas, 1993
S/d in English 'BARI 1993' l.r.
48.0 x 48.0 in (122.0 x 122.0 cm)

INR 600,000 – 750,000
USD 12,500 – 15,625

31

Dhruva Mistry
(b.1957)

Expulsion of Pains
Inkjet on flex, 2002 – 2006
S/d in English 'Dhurva Mistry
2002 – 2006' l.r.
116.6 x 252.5 in (295.5 x 641.3 cm)

INR 1,200,000 – 1,500,000
USD 25,000 – 31,250

This work is based on Picasso's 'Guernica' (1937) which was a response to the bombings on the most ancient town of Basques, Guernica during Spanish Civil war showing the horrors of the war. Picasso's work stands as an epitome of great human tragedy. Dhruva Mistry's interest in the work could be because of the play of planes, and drama that the work offers. By attempting it in red and black ink, Mistry reaffirms the tension in the work.

32

Sailoz Mookherjea

(1907 – 1960)

Palms in Landscape

Pastel & gouache on paper, 1950
Signed in English 'Sailoz' l.l.
18.7 x 13.4 in (47.6 x 34.2 cm)

Chemould Frames label present on verso

INR 800,000 – 1,000,000
National Art Treasure
Non–Exportable Item

Sailoz Mookherjea's works are emblematic of a different stream, also represented by Amrita Sher-Gil, with their focus on the rural subjects, imbibing the swiftness and immediacy of folk art. In 1950 a Retrospective exhibition of his works was held in New Delhi, and a year later his works were also displayed at an exhibition Salon de Mai, Paris.

"In his [Sailoz Mookherjea] treatment of landscape he creates spaces organically by the movement of colour rather than by any clearly indicated recession. The trees evoke a fairy-tale atmosphere and provide the setting for some poetic event. Often the whole composition surges with rhythm now delicate and grave, now tumultuous and free. His arrangements are usually asymmetric and daringly balanced...Sailoz's second period (1949 – 59) includes the mature phase of his art and the paintings of this decade represent the consolidation of the style. His work is much more confident and loose, spontaneous and lyrical." – Jaya Appasamy, rpt. in **Sailoz Mookherjea (Monograph)**, LKA, 1966.

33

A.H. Muller

(1878 – 1952)

Tiger Hunting

Oil on canvas, 1927
S/d in English 'A.H.Muller, 1927' l.r.
23.4 x 34.8 in (59.4 x 88.5 cm)

Condition

Good. Previously restored

INR 800,000 – 1,000,000
USD 16,670 – 20,830

'The Maharaja of Bikaner was fond of hunting. On many an occasion, he took Muller with him for sketching – Muller on one elephant, a photographer on the other and others to help the Maharaja in hunting, forming a cavalcade or a hunting party. On return from hunting, Muller used to draw sketches in the studio of different scenes in hunting and also painted pictures from the photographs taken at the time of actual hunting. The Maharaja was extremely pleased with the paintings of Muller.' – S.B. Shirgaonkar rpt. in *Artist A.H. Muller And His Art* 1975 ExC.

'Poverty finally drove Muller to take employment under the Maharaja of Bikaner in 1922. His assignment was to record hunting trips of the ruler. There was no question of the prince not admiring his talents, but the duties proved onerous. Muller soon gave them up.' – Partha Mitter rpt. in ***Art and Nationalism in Colonial India 1850-1922: Occidental Orientations***,1994 pp. 92-4.

34

L. Munuswamy

(b.1927)

Animals in Composition

Oil on canvas, 1962
Signed in English 'Munuswamy' l.c
49.2 x 47.2 in (125.0 x 120.0 cm)

Condition

Previously restored in October 2006

Provenance

Previously from the Artist's Collection

INR 1,600,000 – 2,000,000
USD 33,330 – 41,670

Illustrated Reference

The Drifting HorizonL L. Munuswamy, DAG, 2007, p71

"In the 60s I painted a number of works which had birds and animals as their motifs. These forms lent themselves to a great extent to the liberty of an artist, to distort, dismember, interlock in a number of ways that satisfied the urge to create... The human form when it is distorted beyond certain limits, becomes crude and vulgarized whereas animal forms lend themselves to innumerable forms that are agreeable and lovable."
– L. Munuswamy, as quoted in The Drifting HorizonL L. Munuswamy, DAG, 2007, p20–21.

35

SHIBU NATESAN

(b.1966)

The Wild Heart

Oil on canvas, 2002
S/d in English 'SHIBU NATESAN 2002'
on verso
47.2 x 59.9 in (120.0 x 152.1 cm)

Inscribed in English 'Oil on canvas,
The Wild Heart, 48 x 60 inch' on verso

Condition

Good, brownish spots on the lower
section

INR 4,000,000 – 5,000,000
USD 83,330 – 104,170

Exhibition Reference

'Cinema Still', Apparao Galleries, New Delhi, 2002

"This painting (Wild Heart) is based on the concept of the film image. Thus the narrative within the image and the sense of frozen movement of a cinema still dominate the way the viewer decodes the layering of the image. The painting was made at the time of the Afghanistan war: oblique reference is made to the conflict through this popular image - guns speak first in lawless country and western movie culture" - Shibu Natesan

Natesan's painting refers to the populist American political imagination that sees its genocidal wars against enemies as having fun killing people. Such attitudes arise from the haloed American pedagogical exercises such as the genre of the American Western film explicitly teaching kids that it's fun to play 'let's gun down some Native Americans'. Ronald Reagan, an actor in Westerns and President of the US in the 1980s, would regularly use popular catch phrases from the Western to 'inspire' his people to go to war.

Landscapes, Cityscapes and Interiors, & the Locked Human Figure

This piece discusses the collection of 16 Lots, part of Select Masterpieces of Indian Modern and Contemporary Art auction. These works of art reflect the conceptual as well as visual journey of post-independence Indian art through till the contemporary, through the specific genre of landscapes, cityscapes and city-interiors.

The assimilation of international modernism in the artistic axioms of Indian artists is one of the important features of the post-independence art scene. These attempts by Indian artists (specifically the Progressives and their successors) can be potentially explored and studied beyond just a "play of texture and creation of planar structures". In the post-colonial vogue, the artists' recourse to a western visual language can be seen through many lenses. Conscious negation of the 'national' in the works of F. N. Souza, S. H. Raza, Akbar Padamsee, Ramkumar & Avinash Chandra in the 1950s when they traveled to Paris, and their systemic identification with the global consciousness can be seen through Franz Fanon's theory (of a native traveling to the mother country / western horizon). They could either obliterate any reference to the "Indian" and become slaves of international formalism and produce stereotyped works, or parcel themselves by including "Indianness", and claim a different dominion which would have implied running against the grain.

Sailoz Mookherjea's 'Palms in Landscape' is a mixture of the swiftness and immediacy of the folk arts and the romantic modernist approach to colour, annotating impressions of the real. As a teacher at Sarda Ukil Art School in Delhi, Mookherjea had been a major influence on many artists. Further, the structured cities of Raza, Padamsee and Ramkumar of the fifties and early sixties, are monotonous cubicles, the maze-like rigid spaces only offering confinements of a defined social existence. In their early works, figures appear in a strenuous relationship with the backdrop. The possibility of a dialogue is broken as they configure as separate entities. The City as backdrop is oppressive with its high structures, grids and routines while the painted figure is numbed and caught in the maze. The human figure is static, usually enjoying an iconic stature in the picture space but ironically resonating their uniconic / ordinary existence. Secure in their contours, defined bodies, their insecurities are reflected through their relationship with the space they inhabit, such as in Santosh's 'Kashmir' or Akbar's poised human figures from his Prophets series and his female nudes and couples, or Ramkumar's "sad" people.

However, when the figure is removed, the cityscape acquires a cumbersome existence. These 'scapes' are further distanced from the 'sense of belonging', as the flattened approach to colour heightens the element of absence or "lack" of sentimentality. There is no romanticism. The objectivity is heightened to erase the platforms of identification. These uncomfortable zones are inhabitable places. These are perhaps strategies to shift focus to the asocial aspects of the city, its seductions and far-end cries. The pictorial surface is jagged by the monotonous yet colourful structures of rising but desolate buildings such as Akbar Padamsee's 'Horizon IV', S. H. Raza's 'Village series', reminiscent of the geometric composition of the famous work Omkareshwar (1948) by H. A. Gade.

Ramkumar's 'Varanasi series' comes after his disaffiliation with politics (he was politically active in France, and was part of the circle of French communists), and the figures in his works have been eliminated. The melancholy of his early works is usurped by the pictorial structure of the cityscape; the objective treatment of Banaras without sentimentality. The difference could be viewed as dealing with portraits of two cities – the industrial city (as represented by the scapes in his early works of the fifties), and the eternal city of Banaras. To use Richard Bartholomew's phrase he was representing "condensed history" in Banaras. The relationship between man and the city gets more complicated with the absence of the human, and the structural remnants of its presence in the holy city of purgation. His later abstract landscapes of the late sixties and seventies fuse in a nostalgic yearning with objectivity.

Amidst the hope of a new India – a new nation, a civil society – the city grew through structures of hope, employment for the poor, with all seductions and lure of luxury offered at the cost of the fragility of human life. Distancing themselves from the turmoil of the nation-building task which was at the helm during the time, the works of many of these artists have undercurrents of guilt, communicated through the choice of their subjects. These artists used "distancing" as a strategic tool for investigating "the alienated".

However, the struggles of the ordinary in these definitive space-structures, amidst a complex nexus of social relations, remain the subject matter for many other artists. In A. Ramachandran's works, the loathsome flesh inhabiting structured spaces is a metaphorical articulation of the stretched bodies / masses caught up in the built spaces. Most of the figures in his works produced during this time don't have heads. The city is a land of action and not thinking. The stretched bodies are portraits of the doers / the city dwellers. Bikash Bhattacharjee's images of a decaying city are reflected through his surreal imagery and the suffocating binds of the city.

The works of three contemporaries – Atul Dodiya, Nataraj Sharma and Baiju Parthan – are emblematic of the different directions that the genre has taken. In Atul Dodiya's 'Roadside with Temple', the local shrine against the textured wall is tactically cornered to left, while the rest of the space is desolate. Shrines and Gods remain an important aspect of Dodiya's work as religion is crucial to the values and aesthetics of the middle-class environment. Using a photo-realist style, Dodiya achieves a stasis in the work, creating the expectation of a visitor or somebody having just visited. These annotations of small town architecture in his later works evolve into popular culture assemblages. Nataraj Sharma adds machines in the landscape as human substitutes, introducing a mechanistic imaginary. His large canvases are dotted with factories, junk iron nuts and bolts – which have become an important aspect of the industrial urban. Baiju Parthan's 'Sun Rising – Patented Landscape' enters into the territorial angst created by the guarded national borders, that on one level become the contours defining the shape of the land / nation, and double up as markers of material differences. The pun in the phrase 'Patented Landscape' cannot be missed as the angels quietly digress from the norms of the mortal world.

36

Akbar Padamsee

(b.1928)

Horizon IV

Oil on board, 1957
S/d in English 'Padamsee 57' l.r.
36.0 x 23.8 in (91.5 x 60.3 cm)

Condition

Preservation work has been carried out in 2008 by Osian's Conservation Department, Mumbai

INR 5,600,000 – 7,000,000
USD 116,670 – 145,830

Padamsee's scapes have registers, distinguished by colours. The tall buildings, houses, occupy the lower register while the upper distant register (ideational distance is created in spite of the flattened surfacial treatment) is almost set in an oblivion, ready to vanish, provides a spatial setting as well as time-cycle of day and night. The absent human figures from these embedded structures add to their rigid maze-like "sui-generis" existence. To see works from the same series 'Horizon I', Horizon II' and 'Horizon III' refer to **Padamsee (monograph)**, Sadanga Series, Vakils.

"...between 1956 and 1959 Akbar painted a series of landscapes and a few still-lifes...His landscapes of this period were distinctly idealized. Most of them were cityscapes, though seldom situated within a recognizable time or place. A sealed hermitage somewhere perhaps, or a holy city of medieval times, illuminated by a golden light. There was nothing familiar or habitable about them. Although one could spot, here and there, steeples, copulas, and chimneys, there were no doors and windows to the buildings, no signs of life. This degree of idealization – one that he never applies to the human figure – made these cityscapes enchanting but at the same time strictly circumscribed...The earliest landscape brought to mind the little medieval towns of France." – Geeta Kapur, rpt. in **Contemporary Indian Artists**, Vikas Publishing, 1978, p104.

PADAMSEE
62

37

Akbar Padamsee

(b.1928)

Landscape

Acrylic on paper, 1962
S/d in English 'PADAMSEE 62' t.r.
25.4 x 19.7 in (64.4 x 49.8 cm)

Inscribed in English 'LANDSCAPE By Akbar Padamsee' on verso

Condition

Minor tear on the upper edge

Provenance

Mukund & Neerja Lath Collection

INR 1,200,000 – 1,500,000
USD 25,000 – 31,250

Exhibition-Auction Reference

The Intuitive-Logic II, Cu. Neville Tuli, HEART, 1997, p66

"The landscapes he painted during his later, grey phase were in contrast panoramic: wide, sweeping views of tropical cities. They carried over the compact structure of geometric forms from the previous landscapes and projected them on to a larger scale. The later landscapes, beginning around 1963, became different. Akbar was slowly finding an equilibrium in his relation to nature, somewhere between an idealised image, a realistic image, and the desired image of a romantic."
- Geeta Kapur, rpt. in rpt. in **Contemporary Indian** Artists, Vikash Publishing, 1978

38

Akbar Padamsee

(b.1928)

Metascape (Diptych)

Oil on canvas, 1995
S/d in English 'Padamsee 95' t.l.
54.0 x 72.4 in (137.4 x 183.7 cm)

Provenance

Private Collection, Mumbai

INR 16,000,000 – 20,000,000
USD 333,330 – 416,670

"Anything that is worth contemplating is possessed of a solitude and indeed Akbar's landscapes are immensely solitary. Girgio de Chirico, an artist whom Akbar has always admired, speaks of two kinds of solitude in works of art: "plastic solitude" which is the contemplative beatitude offered to us by the artist's genius of construction or formal combination; and "metaphysical solitude" in which the artist, presumably treating space as an extended field of his unconscious, projects signs into the infinite and invests it with meaning. In the sense that Akbar regards nature as an objective phenomenon and so restructures it as to give it an aesthetic form – a contemplative beatitude – his genius lies in achieving plastic solitude. The notion of metaphysical solitude in the above sense does not apply to him though he has by a curious coincidence chosen to call his recent landscapes 'metascapes'" – Geeta Kapur, rpt. in **Contemporary Indian Artists**, Vikash Publishing, 1978, p106.

N O R T H
E A S T
S O U T H
1 2 3 4 5 6 7 8 9 0 1 1 2 3 5 8 13 21 34
W E S T

39

BAIJU PARTHAN
(b.1956)

SUN RISING – Patented Landscape
Acrylic and oil on canvas, 2002
S/d in English 'Baiju Parthan 2002'
t.l. and on verso
Titled on verso
47.9 x 48.0 in (121.8 x 122.0 cm)

INR 3,600,000 – 4,500,000
USD 75,000 – 93,750

Exhibition Reference
'Blur', The Fine Art Company, Mumbai and Gallery Espace, New Delhi, 2002

Illustrated Reference
'A Guide to 101 Modern & Contemporary Indian Artists', Amrita Jhaveri, India Book House, 2005, p145

This particular work uses a landscape from a royalty free stock photograph collection and a newspaper photograph of a soldier guarding an army bunker in Kashmir valley. This work reflects my interest in dystopian cyberpunk fiction and is a critique on genetic engineering and a possible future scenario where even the aesthetic spectrum of a vista could be patented and owned by business corporations. A genetically engineered Eden of a probable future with an eclipsed sun rising over a patented landscape, guarded by armed men and owned by business corporations is a dystopian fantasy I use to make critique on the whole approach of using genetic engineering for profit.

"This is one of the early works that make use of imagery appropriated from mainstream media (Newspaper, TV) to create an original artwork. I am not making the claim that I was the first one to do it as the qualifier/ category 'Mediatic Realism' came to be used to identify similar works long before, but certainly was a catalyst in making that kind of work visible and appealing for a large number of art-students who graduated during the early half of 2000. My intention in these media derived works was to take spent images (or images from the media that had lost there contextual potency because it is yesterday's news) and re-contextualise these into original works of art and inject them back into the system/ public imagination." – Baiju Parthan

"Baiju Parthan's art reflects his academic training in engineering, botany, philosophy, comparative mythology, and computer programming. The main theme of his paintings and digital works is the location of the self in a world dominated by technology. Drawing upon such different sources as illuminated manuscripts and computer games, his work represents a quest for individuality, identity, and transcendence in an increasingly uncertain world...In another, 'Sun Rising – (Eden)', 2002 angels descend into a garden of paradise guarded by a soldier. The landscape is near perfect – either genetically modified or digitally manipulated." – Amrita Jhaveri, A Guide to 101 Modern & Contemporary Indian Artists', India Book House, 2005, p145.

1 1 2 3 5 8 13 21 34 55 89 144 233 377
D E O N T O L O G Y

40

Baiju Parthan
(b.1956)

Deontology – Arrival of the knowledge self
Acrylic on canvas, 2007
S/d in English 'Baiju Parthan 2007' t.r.
and on verso
71.7 x 71.6 in (182.3 x 182.0 cm)

Inscribed in English 'DEONTOLOGY
-ARRIVAL OF THE KNOWLEDGE SELF,
ACRYLIC 6ft X 6ft' on verso

INR 4,000,000 – 5,000,000
USD 83,330 – 104,170

Exhibition Reference
'Liquid Memory + Rant: Recent works by Baiju Parthan',
Vadehra Art Gallery, New Delhi, 2007

"This particular series 'deontology' was reflection upon the faceless individual soldier who while in the field is duty bound to perpetrate acts that would be considered atrocities in everyday life. This whole series was about the ethical and moral fallout of these activities once this individual returns to normal everyday life. Along with that there is the known and documented phenomenon of the occurrence of life transforming epiphanies to such individual soldiers in the extremely life threatening and stressful conditions. I have tried to reflect upon these issues in this particular series. This particular work shows a soldier running across a field, either in pursuit or being pursued accompanied by his shadow selves. The painting tries to generate visual depth through layering of imagery and data rather than using perspectival approach. The intention is to suggest an inner idea space rather than a physical space informed by linear perspective." – Baiju Parthan

41

Ganesh Pyne
(b.1937)

Prince
Tempera on paper, 1967
S/d in Bengali 'Ganesh Pyne 67' l.l.
7.6 x 5.9 in (19.3 x 15.0 cm)

INR 1,200,000 – 1,500,000
USD 25,000 – 31,250

A mockery but an intense pathos runs through Pyne's images of prince, ape as prince/ human being. The dramatic tension in his works is created through psychological interiors that he builds through the layers below the surface. There's forever a glow in the dark. Geeti Sen in the introduction to her book 'Image and Imagination' observes, "The subliminal, the psychic, the illusionary nature of human existence can be said to characterize the work of Ganesh Pyne."

42

Ganesh Pyne

(b.1937)

Fossil Man

Ink on paper pasted on paper, 1964
S/d in Bengali 'Ganesh Pyne 64' l.r.
6.9 x 8.8 in (17.0 x 22.5 cm)

Provenance

Previously from the Mukund & Neerja Lath Collection

INR 800,000 – 1,000,000
USD 16,670 – 20,830

Pyne's works give a sense of decay, undergrowth that eats up the substance without one's notice/ knowledge. The skeletal figures hover as if only the memory remains, not the real object. 'Bone' becomes a metaphor for the "remanant" as the process of decaying is still ongoing within the time coordinate of the painting. And the site where these remnants are buried, is visited again and again to remind of something rotting. His works have a strong presence of "Time" as an element that is passing away. This work anticipates his later works such as 'Relics' (1982) where elements like bones and tools emphasize on the process of recollection.

"Death haunts several of the paintings by Ganesh Pyne. It enters stealthily like a fugitive, without notice, like a ghost that melts through closed doors and windows. We can only sense its long hand reaching out, its furtive shadow moving among figures. Death becomes something of an obsession, an intimate friend of the painter." – Geeti Sen, rpt. in **Image and Imagination**, Mapin, 1996, p144.

43

A. Ramachandran

(b.1935)

Untitled

Oil on canvas, *c.*1975
Signed in Malayalam 'Ramachandran' l.l.
68.9 x 64.2 in (174.8 x 162.8 cm)

Condition

Stable cracks on the paint surface

INR 3,600,000 – 4,500,000
USD 75,000 – 93,750

For Works from the same series refer to Rupika Chawla, **Ramachandran: The Art of the Muralist**, Bangalore: Kala Yatra & Sistas Publication 1994

"Sketching from life, his [Ramachandran's] rather dark paintings from the late 1960s and 70s reveal his acute observations of misery in the streets of a socially stratified Delhi, and serve as caustic comments on the human condition. For instance, in Grave Diggers (1977) and Encounter (1967), social concern is expressed through grotesque distortions and elongations of the human body. Sweeper women in Jangpura and prostitutes around Lajpat Nagar in Delhi served as models for his painting entitled Cells (1966) that symbolizes captivity and exploitation. Anonymous and insignificant, his headless figures express the anatomy of pain, their stretched and twisted bodies become markers of their tryst with the harsh reality of the metropolis. The artist's exaggerated illusionist treatment of chiaroscuro accentuates the existential angst and unease of the displaced migrant. Ramachandran's large canvases and mural format served as the expanse of the city in which he portrayed the corporeal human struggle and its endless attempts at release triggered by a utopian desire." – Roobina Karoda and Shukla Sawant, rpt. in **Art and Visual Culture in India 1857-2007**, Marg, 2009, p198.

44

V. Ramesh
(b.1958)

Wages of Samsara
Oil on canvas, 2002
Inscribed in English 'V Ramesh,
Wages of Samsara, Oil on Canvas
2002' on verso
73.2 x 95.2 in (186.0 x 242.0 cm)

INR 1,200,000 – 1,500,000
USD 25,000 – 31,250

Exhibition Reference
'Thousand and one Desires', Threshold Art Gallery, New Delhi, 2004

"The work has quotes from a popular image of hell used in traditional south indian painting and also is a pun on the well known phrase 'wages of sin or samsara'. The images depict various forms of punishment meted out to people engaged in unethical activities raising the dilemma as to what is considered right and what wrong. The painting also has four verses written on the all the four sides of the canvas, verses sourced from an ancient scripture that extol a person to be detached and continue all his worldly activities with a sense of playfulness as well as detachment. The work incorporates not only imagery from popular visual culture but also hints at philosophical truths with a sense of playfulness" – Vedhanbatla Ramesh

45

RAMKUMAR
(b.1924)

Varanasi series
Oil on canvas pasted on board, 1963-64
22.0 x 29.9 in (56.8 x 76.0 cm)

Provenance
Purchased from Gallery Chemould in 1964

INR 5,600,000 – 7,000,000
USD 116,670 – 145,830

"The first contact with Varanasi was very awe inspiring. The humanity was tremendous, a vastness. Old women with heads shaved, pilgrims,... We were sketching, but then I thought that the humanity was such an important part in Varanasi, so it is better to eliminate it, because I would never be able to do justice to it. And so I took out the people, and this went on for about ten years, till about the 1970s...I visited Varanasi about half a dozen times in these years, sketching, to revive and refresh my memories, and of course they change from time to time. At the beginning they were just images of ghats, straightforward, but later they became more complicated and organisational. After all I was maturing as a painter also, and so memories of Varanasi receded."
– Ramkumar in conversation with Neville Tuli, rpt. in **The Flamed Mosaic**, Mapin & HEART, 1997, p365.

"The eternal city: this is how Benaras is often described, even Ram Kumar's Benaras. Eternal, that is, timeless. Yet in his images the process of time is everywhere apparent; in the dissolution of the surface and substance of materials, of the architecture of forms, the shrines and dwellings made by man. For all its impassive façade, his Benaras is like a sprawling relic, a citadel encrusted by the deposit of age and eroded by time."
– Geeta Kapur, rpt. in rpt. in Contemporary Indian Artists, Vikash Publishing, 1978, p. 74.

46

Ramkumar

(b.1924)

Untitled

Oil on canvas, 1969
Signed in Devanagari and dated in English 'Ramkumar 69' l.r.
34.2 x 24.0 in (86.9 x 61.1 cm)

Inscribed in English '18 1969' & camel seal on verso

Provenance

Private Collection, New Delhi

INR 5,600,000 – 7,000,000
USD 116,670 – 145,830

Illustrated Reference

Painting from the same series is illustrated in full colour in N. Tuli's *The Flamed – Mosaic : Indian Contemporary Painting*. New Delhi : HEART and Mapin Publishing 1997. Plate 165, p.224.

"If Ram Kumar's abstractions still have a strange power to move us, it is because they are not built on denial or negation; they carry within them all the stains and bruises of the preceding periods, their sense of grief and solitude, but now they have been somehow transcended; lifted on a different light, where even the whites and greys have a kind of luminosity..." – Nirmal Verma, rpt. in **Ram Kumar: A Retrospective**, ExC, NGMA & Vadehra Gallery, 1993

47

RAMKUMAR
(b.1924)

Varanasi series
Gouache and watercolour on paper, 1981
Signed in Devanagari and dated in English 'Ramkumar 81' on verso
22.9 x 35.6 in (58.1 x 90.4 cm)

INR 5,600,000 – 7,000,000
USD 116,670 – 145,830

After an interlude of abstraction, Ramkumar again returns to Benaras / Varanasi, the holy city of purgation with a different approach this time, annotating its eternal structures – the shrines, the ghats, and its ablutionary waters.

"Ram Kumar, working on the theme of the cityscapes, naturally found the method which recalls a mason and a decorator entirely suitable for his purpose. Hence his extreme faithfulness to it. There are both the architect and the mosaic muralist in him, and his craftsmanship, sober at one level and precious at another, is altogether consistent." – Geeta Kapur, rpt. in **Contemporary Indian Artists**, Vikash Publishing, 1978, p80.

48

S.H. Raza

(b.1922)

Village series

Oil on canvas, 1955
S/d in English 'Raza 55' l.r.
18.1 x 13.2 in (46.1 x 33.5 cm)

Condition

Previously restored

INR 4,000,000 – 5,000,000
USD 83,330 – 104,170

Refer to his other works done in the early 1950s on 'Houses', 'Houses in Landscape' in 'Intuitive Logic: The Next Step', HEART, 1999 p167

Raza began with expressionist landscapes, which became rigid and geometric in the 1950s. For more than a decade, French landscape became a recurrent subject of his work. This phase represents the immediate transition after Raza leaves India for France. The clear tussle between an emphasis on colour and its intuitive expressive powers, and the use of the line with its geometric-structuring potential is evident even at this formative stage.

"S. H. Raza's *Village* in 1956, the year he was awarded the Prix de la Critique, marked the start of his abstraction. The will to encapsulate all within the artistic moment seemed the motivation...Soon the geometric emphasis of the suspended house motifs during the early 1950s would be transformed into a free expressionist structure, dominated by the movements of colour. Thus once again an oscillation between the logic of linearity and the intuitions of colour play would direct Raza's evolution." – Neville Tuli, rpt. in **The Flamed Mosaic**, Mapin & HEART, 1997, p212.

"So much of exposure to a new and different visual culture [referring to the shifting of Raza's base to Paris in 1951] could have easily caused a 'turbulent confusion'. However, instead Raza was able to attain a degree of order and a new kind of landscape started dominating his work. The works of this phase are best described in the words of the French critic Jacques Lassaigne: '... strange un-accountable works, unamenable to any traditional type of art. Timeless landscapes with no accommodation for man; uninhabited, uninhabitable cities, located beyond the confines of the earth, bathed in cold light; schematic houses stretching away in a sinuous line, suspended in the sky beneath a black sun'. The works were well-composed, painstakingly constructed; colours used very poetically and evoked a unique mood of their own. Perhaps the style developed in Bombay was getting refined and expanded in Paris imbibing new elements, creating some new and surprising combinations." – Ashok Vajpeyi, rpt. in **A Life in Art: Raza**, Art Alive Gallery, p64.

49

S.H. Raza

(b.1922)

Prakriti Time and Space

Acrylic on canvas, 2004
S/d in English 'RAZA 04' l.r. and
'RAZA 2004' on verso
39.2 x 39.2 in (99.5 x 99.5 cm)

Inscribed in English '"Prakriti –
time & space" Acryliq on canvas
100 x 100 cm' on verso

INR 5,600,000 – 7,000,000
USD 116,670 – 145,830

"The abstractionist approaches the world as an invitation in code, which rewards the deciphering self with expanded awareness. Raza's practice of symbolic abstraction has as much to do with the nature of symbols as it has with the symbols of nature: he encodes his art with memories of earth, river and rain drawn from his childhood in rural Madhya Pradesh, weaving nostalgia through a consciousness of the sensuous present." – Ranjit Hoskote, rpt. in 'Resonance – Four Claims on Pictorial Space', ExC, Art Musings, 2005.

50

Jamini Roy

(1887 – 1972)

Untitled

Tempera on board, early 1940s
Signed in Bengali 'Jamini Roy' l.r.
17.1 x 12.4 in (43.5 x 32.0 cm)

INR 1,000,000 – 1,250,000
National Art Treasure
Non–Exportable Item

A similar work was exhibited in **Timeless Visions, Contemporary Art of India**, From the Chester and Davida Herwitz Collection.

"With a modernist's sensibility, Roy refined and adapted rural Bengali painting. He took the artists' earth pigments made from local materials, limiting his work to six or seven colours; he painted on clay or lime-coated cloth or paper and on wooden boards using egg tempera or tamarind glue as a binding medium. The works shown in this exhibition exemplify his approach as he applied it to standard religious subjects – the sacred cow; Ravana, the ten-headed villain of the epic Ramayana; and scenes of Jesus from Christian mythology. Jamini Roy found in the materials and styles of indigenous Bengali art a means to create a modern art that was local in its sources, yet deliberate and painterly in its expression, adaptable to themes that transcended the particularities of the religious traditions from which he drew." – Susan S. Bean, rpt. in **Timeless Visions: Contemporary Art of India**, p13.

51

Jamini Roy
(1887 – 1972)

Agni Pariksha
Tempera on cardboard, *c.*1947
Signed in Bengali 'Jamini Roy' l.r.
20.6 x 43.1 in (52.3 x 109.4 cm)

INR 1,200,000 – 1,500,000
National Art Treasure
Non–Exportable Item

A work from the Ramayana series is illustrated in **The Triumph of Modernism, India's Artists and the Avant-garde, 1922-47**, OUP, 2007. Also refer to **Marg 2.1. 1947** for illustrations from the same series.

"Roy's striking formalist pictorial language, his simple monumental images of sari-clad women, madonnas, village dances and domestic animals, have become iconic. The biologist, J.B. S. Haldane once described his paintings as full of simplicity and yet one never tired of gazing at them. Roy himself aspired towards simplicity in an increasingly complex world, as tired adults longed to return to childlike simplicity." – Partha Mitter, rpt. in **The Triumph of Modernism, India's Artists and the Avant-garde, 1922-47**, OUP, 2007, p112.

52

Sadequain

(1930 – 1987)

Alim-e-rang-o-bu (Master of Colour & Fragrance)

Oil on canvas, 1972
S/d in Nashk 'Sadequain 72' l.l.
Inscribed 'Alim-e-rang-o-bu' (Master of colour and fragrance) c.l.
52.7 x 38.6 in (134.0 x 98.0 cm)

Condition

Restoration carried out in 2008 by the Osian's Conservation Department headed by Sanjay Dhar

INR 2,400,000 – 3,000,000
USD 50,000 – 62,500

Lot 52 work titled 'Alim ranga o bu' depicts the creator of colour and fragrance, implying the artist as well as the creator of the cosmos.

Sadequain's images are enactments of an existential drama, a macabre, wherein the desire to be One is willfully suspended. The body is cut into two - be it lovers, artist and his model, or the artist himself. The transcendental is facilitated through this suspension, with forebodings of being doomed. He indulged in the modern Freudian notions of the divisive self (mostly using his own image), and constructed cellular narratives of an artist, an artist's role, 'the creator' but fashions it in his individualistic and daring style. Man and his existential self become his loci. His works can be divided thematically into three main categories – firstly, dealing with the dark and ugly aspects of the self which are sadomasochistic, and secondly Man amidst the cosmic or "the given/ the dictated" order of the environment, struggling with the narrations of mythologies of mankind, and thirdly his calligraphic works. The first two intermingle in subtle ways. Sadequain's obsession with the self is not narcissist in the Greek mythological sense but somewhat like Dante's medieval epic work *Divine Comedy* – the author's journeys of the three realms of the dead – Hell, Purgatory and Paradise – with a living body. Sadequain's visual vocabulary is full of personal symbols such as pen, brush, ink-pot, cactus, mirror and vases.

بول
کہ لب آزاد ہیں تیرے
بول زباں اب تک تیری ہے
تیرا ستواں جسم ہے تیرا
بول کہ جاں اب تک تیری ہے
دیکھ کہ آہنگر کی دکاں میں
تند ہیں شعلے سرخ ہے آہن
کھلنے لگے قفلوں کے دہانے
پھیلا ہر اک زنجیر کا دامن
بول یہ تھوڑا وقت بہت ہے
جسم و زباں کی موت سے پہلے
بول کہ سچ زندہ ہے اب تک
بول جو کچھ کہنا ہے کہہ لے

53

SADEQUAIN
(1930 – 1987)

Bol Ke Lab Azad Hain Tere... (Inspired by the poetry of Faiz Ahmed Faiz)
Mixed media on rexene
Text in Urdu on the painting
78.2 x 48.0 in (198.5 x 122.0 cm)

Condition
Previously restored

INR 2,400,000 – 3,000,000
USD 50,000 – 62,500

This work is based on famous Urdu poet Faiz Ahmed Faiz's poetry 'Bol, Ke Lab Azad Hain Tere'. Faiz's revolutionary poem asks the man to speak up when there's still time. Sadequain provides visual imagery to his words with a chained man with lips stitched. The pen and ink in protagonist's hands are his real weapons, provoking him to break the silence, and make the mark.

The contradictions inherent in Sadequain's persona as an artist make a singular assessment of his works a difficult task – his company of the powerful and elite, along with his popularity among the commoners and thus, the title "*awami painter*" bestowed to him. Sadequain's role in modern art of the subcontinent is illustrious as the harbinger of renaissance in the calligraphic painting. In his works he traces the blasphemous journeys of an anguished soul/ ego, along with other laurels such as illustrating Ghalib's verses (1968 – 69), Faiz Ahmed Faiz's verses (1970) and lithographs for Albert Camus's book *The Stranger* (1964).

54

G.R. Santosh
(1929 – 1997)

Kashmir
Mixed media on canvas, 1959
Signed in Devanagari and dated in English 'Santosh 59' l.l.
34.1 x 54.4 in (86.5 x 138.2 cm)

Remnants of India Fine Arts & Craft Society, New Delhi label present on verso

Condition
Stable cracks on the paint surface

INR 1,200,000 – 1,500,000
USD 25,000 – 31,250

In 1950, Santosh joined the Progressive Arts Association in Kashmir, formed as a result of painter S. H. Raza's efforts to mobilize Kashmiri painters. In 1954, he won the government scholarship to study Fine Arts under painter N. S. Bendre at the MS University, Baroda and was a recipient of National Award in 1957. G.R. Santosh's Kashmiri landscapes are examples of his astute pictorial idiom. He creates tension through his stiff lines, and planar application of colours helps in creating recessive patterns on the picture surface. "This semi-abstract work done in semi-cubist style shows mother and child (shikarawalas) with their hutment in the background and these hutments are built on a platform made of wood usually on the banks and the back waters of the Dal Lake. Also seen is a shikara on the right corner of the work. This impasto style work is created on the canvas not with a knife but with the shaving blade. My father always thought that a blade gave him precise strokes more than the knife" says Shabir Santosh. The relationship created between the figure and the scape is an uneasy one.

"In Baroda Santosh began the serious study of oil painting; he now painted both in water colour and oil. From purely cubistic efforts he passed on to essentially flowing, linear form. Santosh's painting of this period featured the human figure with their characteristic oval or round head and occasional traces of cubism in the shapes and thrusts. I personally felt then that he faced the threat of possible stylization. Soon, however, the figure became barely suggestive and attenuated, finally disappearing altogether. Landscape, which had been a backdrop to the figures, became prominent and in course of time pushed out the figure once and for all." – S. A. Krishnan, rpt. in 'A Painter of Kashmir: Santosh', **LKA 34**, June 1987, p75.

"In the early to mid-1950s he [G. R. Santosh] did semi-cubistic works of awkwardly determined figures, such as farmers in the field, mother and child and so on – something that was being attempted with variations, by a number of artists, from Ramkinkar Baij to N. S. Bendre." – Gayatri Sinha, rpt. in 'A remarkable artist, a remarkable show', The Hindu, 9th February 2001.

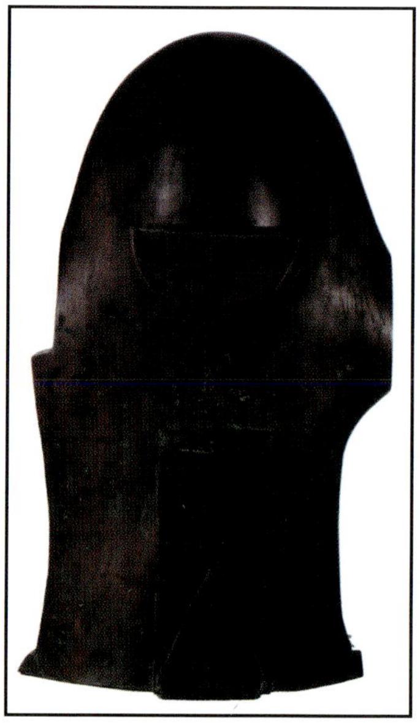

55

Himmat Shah

(b.1933)

Head

Bronze

20.1 x 11.0 x 13.6 in (51.0 x 28.0 x 34.5 cm)

INR 2,400,000 – 3,000,000

USD 50,000 – 62,500

Himmat Shah's terracotta and bronze heads have a special place in the history of Modern Art. They represent a sustained body of deep introspective creativity, tackling the most familiar artistic source of inspiration - the human head, and yet abstracting it to a unique minimalism, head after head, while maintaining its virile and universal intellectual force .

In recent years a few of the terracotta's have been cast in bronze allowing some of the top international collectors to incorporate Himmat Shah in their collection, given the scarcity and fragile nature of the fired terracotta work.

56

NATARAJ SHARMA

(b.1958)

Roadmaker

Oil, acrylic and charcoal on paper and canvas pasted on masonite board, 1995 – 1998
30.8 x 57.2 in (78.4 x 145.2 cm)

Inscribed in English 'NATARAJ, ROADMAKER, OCT- 95- MAY 96- JAN 98, OIL, ACRYLIC AND CHARCOAL ON PAPER AND CANVAS, Year: 2004' on verso of board

INR 1,600,000 – 2,000,000
USD 33,330 – 41,670

"Before I came to Vadodara, I lived in Bangalore where I did a lot of figurative, urban images. Moving to the outskirts of this city in western India, I was confronted with a primal, elemental landscape dotted by factories that looked extremely desolate in the summer. The world might be at the forefront of technology but for us these outdated factories and chunky machines are an everyday reality. I am not here to make moralistic statements about our oil-stained and garbage strewn landscapes. I want to seek the peculiar beauty of these desolate structures. Their presence is comforting." – Nataraj Sharma, rpt. in **Real in Realism**, ExC, Vadehra Art Gallery, 2002.

"...human protagonists were virtually eliminated by Nataraj. His works were filled with images of violated, distorted and confused landscapes – denatured under the intrusion of primitive but rapacious industry. Old fashioned machines and tools wounded the terrain in these paintings, yet in the process, they assumed, almost imperceptibly, the traits of the people who used them." – Marta Jakimowicz-Karle, rpt. in 'The Mechanics of Painting', Art India Magazine, Vol. IV, Issue 3, July-Sept 1999.

"A ground, a landscape. A foreground viewed from the top, the far horizon seen through the eyes of a low flying bird. At this distance, and with this distancing, the earth reveals herself. In these drylands, without the cosmetic cover of vegetation, I see the earth's face, twisting and turning, ancient and awesome. I see the colours of the earth-areas of dazzling brightness and diffused shadows. Fences, like rows of matchsticks, transform the earth into property.

On Sama Road (Vadodara) a familiar upheaval goes on. Gouged up earth, the earth's innards lie exposed. Looking down into the trenches, I see large drainage pipes, hard and cylindrical, embraced by sinuous electric cables. I take a turn to the right and pass through some desperate shanties before falling upon a magnificent, convoluted vision. A wasteland ravaged and desolate. An open view through to the horizon. Eroded gullies and a deep cleft filled with stagnant water. This whole rough and tumbled ground criss-crossed by a network of trembling footpaths." – Nataraj Sharma, rpt. in **Nataraj: Recent Works 1994-96**, ExC

Souza 1950

57

F.N. Souza

(1924 – 2002)

Untitled

Oil on board, 1960
S/d in English 'SOUZA 1960' l.r.
21.9 x 15.7 in (55.7 x 40.0 cm)

INR 4,000,000 – 5,000,000
USD 83,330 – 104,170

"What is it that provides the raw edge to Souza's men? Totally devoid of sentimentality, even when he is portraying himself, there is a detached observation of human degradation...These foetus faces, as Souza would have them, are the essential condition of human beings, of men without redemption." – Yashodhara Dalmia, rpt. in **The Making of Modern Indian Art**, OUP, 2001, p84

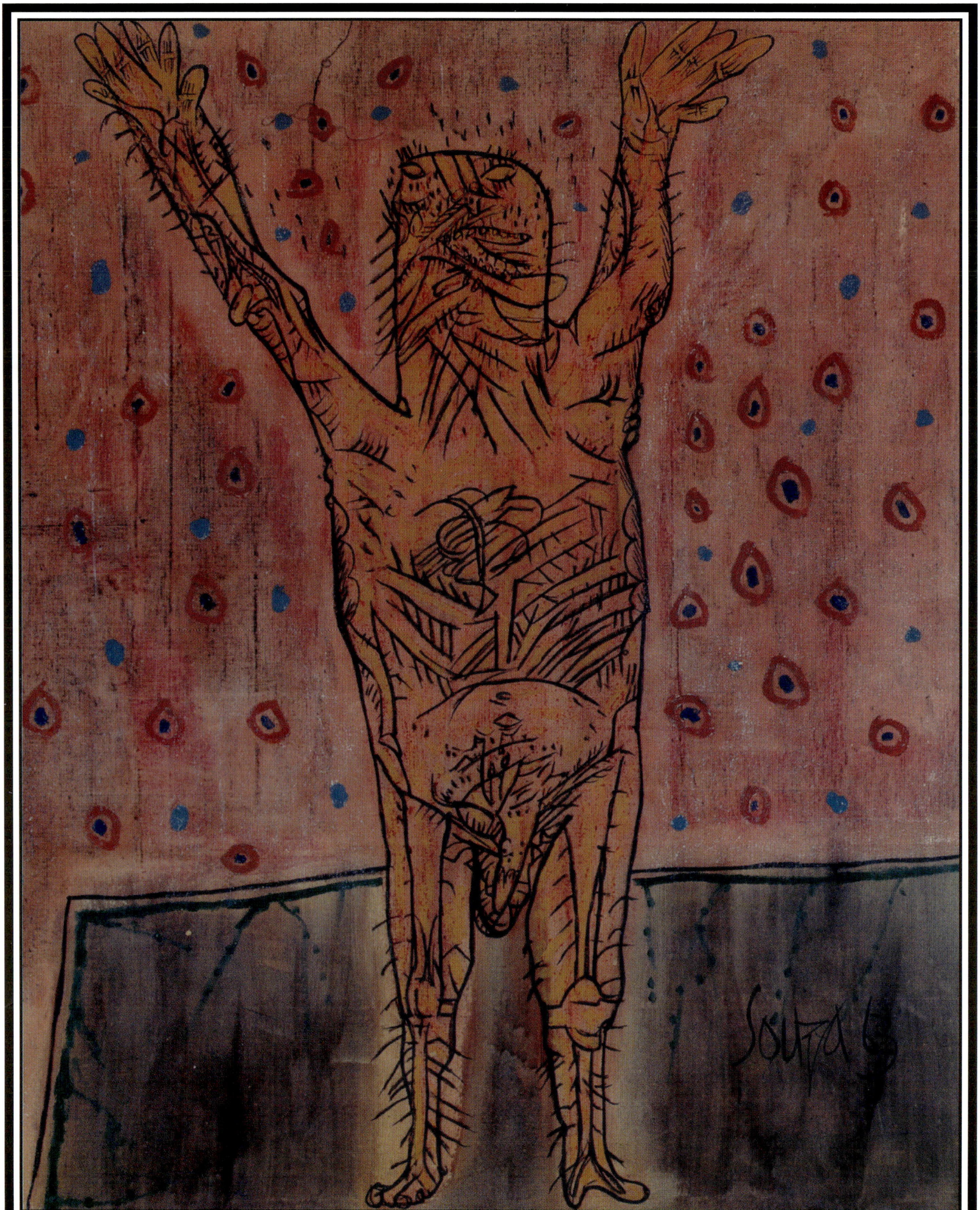

58

F.N. Souza

(1924 – 2002)

Evolution of Apollo

Oil on canvas, 1963
S/d in English 'Souza 63' l.r.
54.0 x 43.2 in (137.2 x 109.5 cm)

Inscribed in English 'Evolution of Apollo, 1963, 46" x 54"' on verso

INR 8,000,000 – 10,000,000
USD 166,670 – 208,330

According to Greek mythology, Apollo's birth is seen as his emergence from beneath the earth to the sunlit surface as his mother Leto searches for a place to give birth. Souza plays with this symbolic ascent journey of Apollo, the Sun God, who also cures epidemic diseases. Also to be noted is the fact that it was in the early sixties that NASA began its historic space programme 'Apollo' to place man on the Moon, after John F. Kennedy's famous proclamation on May 25, 1961.

"That Souza belongs to the category of the rebel is evident from the themes and style of his paintings and from his personal behaviour. Flaming and raging through the years he has succeeded in presenting himself as the Fallen Angel driven from the Kingdom of God, as Lucifer avenging himself by rending the veil of sublimity...
The rebel in this form attempts to prove, by his act of continual transgression, the need for a metaphysical insurrection in which God is blasphemed and then killed off, the better to reckon with the business of human life on earth." – Geeta Kapur, rpt. in **Contemporary Indian Artists**, Vikas Publishing, 1978, p38.

Terms and Conditions

The Terms and Conditions set out below are the terms and conditions applicable to the Auction and are binding on the Purchasers, intending Purchasers, Sellers and Osian's – Connoisseurs of Art Private Limited (Osian's).

These Terms and Conditions and all other contents in the Auction Publication are subject to amendment by Osian's from time to time by the posting of notices or by oral announcements made during the Auction. By participating in the Auction, in person or otherwise, intending Purchasers, Purchasers and Sellers agree to be bound by these Terms and Conditions.

1. Definitions

Auction: Auction shall mean the private Auction of Lots held by Osian's wherein each Lot is sold to a Purchaser at the Purchase Price along with and taxes as applicable.

Auction Publication: Auction Publication shall mean this publication and shall include any advertisement, brochure, textual, pictorial and educational information, estimates or price list published by Osian's in respect of the Auction.

Lot: Lot shall mean any item(s), being one or more paintings, photographs, etchings, engravings, lithographs, oleographs, film publicity material, lobby cards, posters, books or works of art being offered for sale at the Auction and, in particular, the item(s) described against any lot number in the Auction Publication.

Auctioneer: Auctioneer shall mean any person(s) who is/are nominated by Osian's to be the Auctioneer(s) at the Auction.

Hammer Price: Hammer Price shall mean the amount of the highest Bid accepted by the Auctioneer in relation to a Lot excluding the Buyer's Premium and any taxes applicable.

Purchase Price: Purchase Price shall mean the Hammer Price in respect of a Lot sold at the Auction together with the Sales Tax/VAT payable if any, plus Buyer's Premium (Commission earned by Osian's) including Service Tax if any and Freight, Packing, Insurance, warehousing and such other charges, expenses and payments due from the Purchaser of such Lot.

Seller: Seller shall mean any person, being an individual, artist, collector, organisation or art gallery, including Osian's, owning a Lot and depositing such Lot with Osian's for Sale at the Auction.

Bid: Bid shall mean an offer made to Osian's by an intending Purchaser to purchase a Lot, either in person at the Auction, or by a Written Bid Form received by Osian's on or before 3.00 p.m. Indian Standard Time on the day of the Auction, on the telephone during the Auction or through an authorized representative at the Auction.

Purchaser: Purchaser shall mean the person with the highest bid accepted by the Auctioneer for a Lot, who agrees to purchase such Lot at the Purchase Price and immediately pays to Osian's, at least 20% of the Purchase Price as advance payment for the Lot to be purchased.

2. Role of Osian's

Sale of Lots at the Auction are undertaken by Osian's as an agent for the Seller except when it wholly or partially owns any lot as principal or has made a financial commitment in respect of, and puts it up for sale as a Seller.

3. The Sale

Sale of Lots shall be by auction at the Hammer Price and Facilitation Charges. MVAT and other taxes, levies and duties shall be charged separately, if applicable. The taxes shall be collected and paid by Osian's on behalf of the Seller.

In the event of Lots to be exported outside India by Osian's, no VAT will be charged to such Purchaser and Service Tax will also be not applicable on the Buyer's Premium commission. However, other services such as Freight, Shipping and Insurance will be payable by such purchaser.

In the event the Lots are sold within state of Maharashtra, MVAT in Maharashtra will be charged @ 12.5% on paintings and sculpture and nil rate for books.

Purchasers from outside the state of Maharashtra will be charged Central Sales Tax @ 2% against Form 'C'. In the event of the Purchaser not being able to provide Form 'C', Central Sales Tax will be charged @ 12.5% except for sale of books which will be at nil rate.

Form 'C' shall be issued by the Purchaser where applicable alongwith the payment for the lots purchased. The delivery of the Lots purchased will not be effected till Form 'C' is received by Osian's.

However courier and octroi charges if applicable will be charged extra.

4. The Purchaser

The person making the highest Bid accepted by the Auctioneer for a Lot and immediately paying to Osian's, at least 20% of the Purchase Price as advance payment for the Lot proposed to be purchased, will be the Purchaser of such Lot at the Purchase Price. Every intending Purchaser shall be deemed to act as principal unless there is in force a written acknowledgement by Osian's that such intending Purchaser is an authorised representative acting as an agent on behalf of a named principal.

Subject to the Auctioneer's discretion, the striking of his hammer marks the acceptance of the highest Bid as the Hammer Price.

Once the bid is accepted, no rejection claim will be entertained and accepted for any reason whatsoever. Any dispute during the Auction will be settled at the Auctioneer's absolute discretion. The conclusion of the contract for sale between the Seller, Purchaser and Osian's will be on receipt of full payment and dispatch of Lot(s) by Osian's.

5. The Bidding

Before the Auction, Osian's will accept Written Bids for each Lot from intending Purchasers. If at the Auction, no Bids higher than the starting Bid are offered, that Bid shall become the Hammer Price, subject to such Bid being higher than the minimum reserve price for such Lot. The minimum reserve price shall be determined and fixed jointly by Osian's and the Seller. In the event of higher Bids being offered, the Auction will continue by means of Paddle Bidding explained in Clause 7.

6. Absentee Bidding

i. If instructed and where possible, Osian's will, for the convenience of intending Purchasers provide the service of executing Bids and advising intending Purchasers. This service shall be free. The intending Purchaser shall mention the maximum amount till which he/she is authorising Osian's to Bid as the Hammer Price for every Lot on his behalf. Lots will be bought as cheaply as is allowed by such other bids and the minimum reserve. In the event of identical bids, the earliest will take precedence. Buy or unlimited bids shall not be accepted by Osian's. Intending Purchasers are requested to use the bidding slips provided, to check Lot numbers and descriptions and to bid as early as possible. The Bid Price mentioned on the bidding slip shall be the amount up to which the intending Purchaser would bid if the intending Purchaser were to attend the Auction.

ii. Bids, when placed by telephone, shall be accepted at the caller's risk and only if confirmed by the Written Bid Form reaching Osian's before the scheduled time as mentioned in Clause 1. Osian's is not responsible for the failure of any telephone bid for any reason whatsoever. Osian's reserves the right to record on tape conversations of telephone bids.
iii. Alternative bids should be indicated by using the word OR between lot numbers. Then if the intending Purchaser's bid on an early Lot is successful, Osian's will not continue to bid on other lots for the intending Purchaser. Or, if the early bids are unsuccessful, Osian's will continue to execute bids for alternative lots until a bid is successful. Bids must always be placed in the same order as the lot numbers in the Auction Publication.
iv. Purchasers will be notified with invoice and Purchase Price within two days after the Auction and the Purchaser will within next twelve days make full payment to Osian's.
v. For overseas and outstation bidders, whether present or absent at the Auction venue, the Lots will be dispatched by Osian's at the Purchaser's risk. Osian's liability will cease as soon as the Lots are handed over to the carriers for onward dispatch to the Purchaser.

7. Paddle Bidding

i. To assist the progress of the Auction, all intending Purchasers are required to register for a bidding paddle before the commencement of the Auction. All intending purchasers should bring with them some means of identification to the satisfaction of Osian's.
ii. All intending Purchasers should provide a credit reference through their Bankers and details on name and address of bank and account number. Intending Purchasers are also expected to provide a reference of any member of the Advisory Board of Osian's listed in the Auction Publication, who is personally known to him/her.
iii. The numbered paddles must be used to indicate the intending Purchaser's bids to the Auctioneer during the Auction. Purchaser of any Lot, shall ensure that his bidding paddle can be seen by the Auctioneer and that it is his number that is called out. Should there be any doubts as to a Bid, the Hammer Price or the Purchaser, the Auctioneer's attention should be drawn to it immediately.
iv. All Lots sold shall be invoiced to the name and address given against the issue of the numbered bidding paddles and cannot be transferred to other names and addresses. Please do not mislay the paddle; in the event of loss or misplacement, the staff at the registration desk should be informed immediately. At the end of the sale, paddles should be returned to the registration desk.

8. Minimum Reserves

All Lots in the Auction are subject to a minimum reserve which is a confidential minimum value below which the Seller is unwilling to sell the Lot. The minimum reserve shall, in no circumstances, exceed the lower pre-sale estimate mentioned in the Auction Publication or revisions as mentioned in Clause 9. Osian's retains the right to open the bidding on behalf of the Seller and continue to bid up to the value of the minimum reserve.

9. Pre-sale Estimates

Pre-sale listed estimates of probable Hammer Prices of each Lot are intended as a guide for intending Purchasers. Any bid between such listed estimates would, in Osian's opinion, offer a fair chance of success. However all Lots, depending on the degree of competition, can realise prices either above or below such listed estimates. Estimates by Osian's are statements of opinion only, made by Osian's for the convenience of intending Purchasers. Estimates are subject to revision by Osian's from time to time.

10. Minimum Increment

The Auctioneer shall have the right to refuse any bid which does not exceed the previous bid by at least 5–10 percent or by such other proportion as the Auctioneer shall in his absolute discretion deem appropriate.

11. Buyer's Premium (Commission)

Buyer's Premium will be charged by Osian's in addition to the Hammer Price. Such premium will be computed as mentioned below on total Hammer Price of all the lots purchased by a Purchaser in an auction.

Total Hammer Price	Buyers Premium (%)
Upto Rs. 10.00 Crore	20
From Rs. 10.01 Crore to 15.00 Crore	17.5
Above Rs. 15.00 Crore	15

Service Tax @ 10.30% will be charged on Buyer's Premium.

12. Conclusion of Sale

On the Sale of a Lot, the Purchaser of such Lot shall:
i. immediately furnish to Osian's his/her name and address and, if requested, proof of identity;
ii. immediately pay to Osian's, a sum not less than twenty percent of the Purchase Price for the Lot to be purchased;
iii. immediately execute a Sale Contract in the form acceptable to Osian's
iv. within fourteen days from the date of the Auction, pay to Osian's the balance of the Purchase Price along with Sales Tax/ VAT, if applicable.

13. Foreign Purchasers

Any Purchaser who is a foreign national or entity, a non-resident Indian (whether or not an Indian citizen) (NRI) or Overseas Corporate Body (OCB) shall make such payment in convertible foreign currency or in Indian Rupees from NRO accounts in accordance with the Foreign Exchange Management Act, 1999 unless exempted by the Government of India.

14. Exportable Items

All relevant export documents for exportable Lots shall have to be procured by the Purchasers. Osian's shall in no way be responsible for procurement of the same. However, Osian's will endeavour to assist the Purchaser in facilitating the process of procurement of export documents.

15. Non-Exportable Items

All 'Non-Exportable Lots' have 'Non-Exportable Lot' written below the Lot's caption details. These items cannot be exported or taken out of India by the buyer/s or their agents, if any. Osian's shall in no way be responsible in case of any loss, damage or legal consequences incurred by any other person or entity due to export of such non-exportable items, after sale by Osian's.

16. Ownership of Lots

The ownership of a Lot purchased shall not pass on to the Purchaser of such Lot until the Purchaser makes full payment of the Purchase Price plus applicable taxes as required by Osian's. The ownership of the Lot to the Purchaser shall not result in transfer of intellectual property rights and copyright in the Lot in favour of the Purchaser.

17. Collection of Purchases

i. The Purchaser shall at his/her own expense take delivery of the Lot purchased not later than 14 days after the date of the Auction, but not before payment of the Purchase Price plus taxes as required by Osian's.
ii. The Purchaser shall solely be responsible for packing, insurance, and forwarding of the Lot(s) purchased by him/her.
iii. The Purchaser shall be liable to pay Osian's all removal, storage and insurance charges imposed by Osian's on the Lot not collected by the Purchaser within 14 days after the date of the Auction. Demurrage charges will be levied @ 1 percent of the purchase Price per month or pro rata thereof from the fifteenth day after the date of the Auction.
iv. On specific instructions of local Purchasers, Osian's may undertake packing, handling and insurance. All costs towards the same as determined by Osian's shall be borne fully and paid by the Purchaser. This service is being given solely as a courtesy to local Purchasers, and will be undertaken at Osian's discretion. In no event will Osian's be liable for damage, regardless of cause. While Osian's may recommend packers and shippers, Osian's shall not in any way be responsible for their errors, omissions or negligence whatsoever.
However, in case of inter-state sale or export sale, the costs and expenses towards insurance, packing, octroi, handling and transportation shall be undertaken by Osian's, which shall be reimbursed by Purchasers at a price determined by Osian's.

18. Purchaser's Responsibilities for Lots Purchased

The Purchasers shall be solely responsible for loss or damage to Lots purchased after the period specified in Clause 17 (i), and neither Osian's or it's employees or agents shall thereafter be responsible for any loss or damage of any kind, whether caused by negligence or otherwise, while any Lot is in the custody or under control of Osian's.

19. Provenance

All intending Purchasers are hereby advised that the Seller shall provide Osian's for each Lot, a guarantee letter that such Lot is created/owned by such Seller. Due care and diligence has been taken by Osian's to verify the Provenance/Declaration authenticity and origin of each Lot.
In the event of any person raising objection to the Lot to be counterfeit, fake, forgery, stolen or smuggled during the process of the same being auctioned, Osian's shall at its discretion withdraw the work from the auction and shall not be responsible for any criminal or civil proceedings being initiated. Osian's shall retain the custody of the Lot for a period of six weeks so as to assist the investigating agency, if any person with regard to that Lot initiates any proceedings.

20. Guarantee in respect of Counterfeit Lot

If, after sale by Osian's, any Lot is proved to be counterfeit or fake, Osian's undertakes to set aside the sale and refund to the Purchaser the amount paid by him in connection with the Lot subject to the following conditions:

i. that within one (1) year of the date of the sale, the Purchaser shall notify Osian's in writing of the number of the Lot, the date of the Auction at which it was purchased and the reasons as to why the Purchaser considers the Lot to be counterfeit along with a bonafide expert's report clearly specifying reasons for such claim. Osian's shall not to be liable to any claims after completion of the period of one (1) year.
ii. that the Purchaser is able to transfer good title to Osian's free from any third party claims arising after the date of sale to him/her.
iii. that the Purchaser returns the Lot to Osian's in the same condition in all respects as at the date of sale by Osian's.

On receipt of the claim, Osian's shall have the right to request the Purchaser to obtain at the Purchaser's cost, the reports of two (2) independent experts in the field, mutually acceptable to the Purchaser and Osian's, setting out the reasons in full as to why the Lot in question is considered to be counterfeit.
Osian's agrees that it will give due consideration to any such expert reports. However, Osian's reserves the right to seek additional independent advice/report and/or submit such Lot to Osian's' Authentication Committee for reconsideration, before making its final determination as to whether the Lot is counterfeit or genuine and shall not be bound by any expert report submitted by the Purchaser.
If Osian's accepts the claim of the Purchaser that the Lot is counterfeit, Osian's shall refund to the Purchaser the Hammer Price and Buyer's Premium as paid by the Purchaser to Osian's at the time of purchase excluding taxes, duties and levies paid/payable to any Government or Municipal Authority by Osian's provided always that the benefit of the guarantee and the refund amount is not capable of being transferred and is solely for the benefit of the purchaser.
Osian's shall in no way be responsible for any loss, damage or any other liability incurred by any third party due to genuineness, origin, attribution, condition, ownership, provenance, age or estimated price of any Lot.

21. Condition of Lots

All Lots are auctioned as shown, with all faults, imperfections and errors of description. Osian's shall not be in any way responsible for errors of description or for genuineness or authenticity of any Lot, or for any fault or defect in it. Intending Purchasers should inspect a Lot before bidding to determine its condition, size, or whether or not it has been repaired, restored or damaged. Osian's has referred to restoration in works where it has been brought to its knowledge. The absence of reference to damage and/or restoration does not imply that the Lot is free from defects. Any representation in the Auction Publication pertaining to authorship, origin, date, age, size, medium, attribution, provenance, condition, or estimated price is a statement of opinion only.

22. Non-payment or Failure to Collect Purchases

If the Purchase Price for any Lot is not received by Osian's in full or if any Lot is not collected by its Purchaser in accordance with Clause 12, Osian's shall be entitled to -
i. charge 1% of the Purchase Price or pro rata thereof as demurrage charges per month;
ii. dispose of the Lot as Osian's deems appropriate, without giving any notice to the Purchaser and forfeit all amounts paid by the Purchaser in respect of such Lot;
iii. proceed against the Purchaser for damages for breach of contract;
iv. rescind the Sale of that or any other Lot or Lots sold to the defaulting Purchaser at the Auction;
v. resell the Lot or cause it to be resold by public auction or private sale and the defaulting Purchaser shall pay to Osian's any resulting deficiency in the purchase price (after deduction of any part payment and addition of resale costs and charges) and any surplus shall belong to Osian's.

vi. charge interest at a rate not exceeding two percent per month on the Purchase Price to the extent the Purchase Price or any part thereof remains unpaid for more than fourteen days after the date of the auction;
vii. retain that or any other Lot sold to the same Purchaser and release such Lot or any other Lot only after receiving payment of the Purchase Price in respect of each Lot purchased by the Purchaser;
viii. reject or ignore any bids made by or on behalf of the defaulting Purchaser at any future auction or sale or obtain a deposit from the Purchaser before accepting any bids in future; and
ix. to apply any proceeds of sale then or at any other time becoming due to the defaulting Purchaser towards settlement of the Purchase Price and to exercise lien on any property of the defaulting Purchaser which is in Osian's possession for any purpose.

23. Right to Refuse Admission

Osian's shall have the right, at its discretion, to refuse admission or attendance to any person at the place of auction.

24. Undertaking of Seller

Osian's shall handle each Lot, and the Purchaser shall purchase such Lot on the basis of the Seller's undertaking that:
a. the Seller is the sole owner of the Lot with an unrestricted right to transfer title to the Purchaser free from all third party rights or claims;
b. the Seller has complied with all requirements legal or otherwise relating to any export or import of the Lot and has notified Osian's in writing that there is no failure by any third party to comply with such a requirement in the past; and
c. the Seller has notified Osian's in writing of any material alterations to the Lot and of any concerns, expressions or claims made by third parties in relation to the ownership, additions or attributions of the Lot.
In case any of the a, b, c is incorrect, and due to the incorrect information provided by the Seller, any third party institutes any claim or institutes any proceedings for compensation for damages then the Seller undertakes to indemnify Osian's and keep Osian's indemnified from time to time against any such claim for compensation or damages.

25. Discretion of Osian's

Osian's has absolute discretion without giving any reason, to refuse any Bid, to combine any two or more Lots, to withdraw any Lot from the Auction, and in case of dispute to put up any Lot for auction again.

26. Copyright

No warranties or representations are made by either the Seller or Osian's as to any Lot is subject to copyright, nor as to whether the Purchaser acquires any copyright in any Lot sold.

27. Right to Share Information

Osian's reserves the right, if required, to share all information related to the sale, the seller, sales value and the buyer if requisitioned/demanded by any Government authority/ies.

28. Honorarium for Living Artists

Osian's shall, at its discretion, pay an honorarium of one half percent (0.5%) of the Hammer Price to all living artists for works created by them but consigned for sale by other owners. The honorarium shall be payable from the income generated by Osian's through sale of the Lot. The honorarium is void in the event of the Lot being brought in or remaining unsold.

The honorarium is at the discretion of Osian's and Osian's shall not be held liable for any delay in payment or, for any reason whatsoever, non-payment of this honorarium. This honorarium is only for living artists and heirs of deceased artists shall not be eligible to receive this honorarium.

29. Waiver

If part of these terms and conditions is found by any Court to be invalid, illegal or unenforceable, that part may be discontinued and the rest of the terms and conditions shall continue to be binding and enforceable to full extent permissible by law.

30. Default by a Party

Osian's shall not be responsible for any default of these terms and conditions or otherwise by any of the Sellers, intending Purchasers or the Purchasers.

31. Notice

Any notice by Osian's to a Seller, intending Purchaser or the Purchaser may be served by mail or by facsimile with confirmation of receipt and if served by mail shall be deemed to have been duly received by the addressee forty-eight hours after mailing.

32. Governing Laws, Jurisdiction and Arbitration

These terms and conditions shall be governed and construed in accordance with Indian law. All transactions to which these terms and conditions apply and all matters connected with shall also be governed by Indian law and subject to (Bombay) jurisdiction of courts at Mumbai.

All disputes arising out of these terms and conditions or any disputes arising out of any transaction between Osian's and/or the Seller, and/or the Purchaser, and/or the Intending Purchaser shall be referred to an arbitration panel comprising of three arbitrators, one appointed by each party and the third umpire appointed by the arbitrators and the arbitration proceedings shall be governed by Arbitration and Conciliation Act, 1996. The place of arbitration shall be Mumbai. The arbitration proceedings shall be conducted in English language.

33. Headings

Headings in the Terms and Conditions do not form part of the terms and conditions and are for convenience only.

34. Antiquities

It is a statutory requirement that all antiquities consigned to Osian's for public auction by it should be such as have been registered with the Archeological Survey of India (ASI) by the Owners/Consigners thereof. While Osian's will not be held liable for the fulfillment of this requirement, it will endeavour to facilitate the process where able to do so and upon request from the Owners/Consigners.

Osian's-Connisseurs of Art Private Limited is licenced by the A.S.I. to sell Antiquities in the state of Maharashtra & Delhi.

A Select Bibliography from the Osian's Centre for Archiving, Research and Development (CARD) Collection.

Books

Adajania, Nancy. ***T V Santhosh Unresolved Stories 2004-2007***. New Delhi, The Guild, 2007.
Ali, J Sultan. ***J Sultan Ali.*** Madras: Cholamandal Artists, 1979.
---. ***Search Beyond Creativity.*** Madras: The Author, 1982.
---. ***Sultan Ali Dialogue with Three Art Critics.*** Madras: Sultan Ali Art Gallery, ---.
Ali, Wijdon (Ed.). ***Contemporary Art from the Islamic World.*** London: Scorpion, 1989.
Andhra Pradesh Lalit Kala Akademi. ***K Laxma Goud.*** Hyderabad: AP-LKA, 1991.
Appasamy, Jaya. ***Sailoz Mookherjea.*** New Delhi: LKA, 1966.
---. ***Nandalal Bose 1882–1966.*** New Delhi: NGMA, 1983.
---. ***Critical Vision: Selected Writings.*** New Delhi: LKA, 1985.
Archer, W G. ***India and Modern Art.*** Bombay: Marg, ---.

Bartholomew, R L (Ed.). ***Nandalal Bose: A Collection of Essays – Centenary Volume.*** New Delhi: LKA, 1983.
Bartholomew, Richard and Kapur, S Shiva. ***Maqbool Fida Husain.*** New York: Harry N Abrams, ---.
Bean, Susan S. ***Timeless Visions: Contemporary Art of India: From the Chester and David Herwitz Collection.*** Massachusetts: Peabody Essex Museum, ---.
Beier, Ulli. ***J Sultan Ali. Ed. by R L Bartholomew***. New Delhi: LKA, 1983.
---. ***Sultan Ali: India.*** ---: Institute of Papua New Guinea Studies, 1976.
Bern, Kunstmuseum (Ed.). ***Horn Please: Narratives In Contemporary Indian Art.*** Germany: Hatje Cantz, 2007.
Bhalla, Alok and Shivadas, Vidya (Ed.). ***Ram Kumar: The Face and Other Stories***. New Delhi, VAG, 2004.
Bhattacharya, Asok K. ***Calcutta Paintings.*** Calcutta: DICA-GWB, 1979.
Bickelmann, Ursula and Ezekiel, Nissim. ***Artists Today: East-West Visual Arts Encounter.*** Bombay: Marg, 1987.
Bose, Nandalal. ***Vision and Creation. Tr. by Kalpati Ganapati Subramanyan.*** Calcutta: Visva-Bharati, 1999.
---. ***Rupavali I.*** Calcutta: Visva Bharati, 2000.

Chaithanya, Krishna. ***History of Indian Painting: The Modern Period.*** New Delhi: Abhinav, 1994.
Chatterji, Ram (Ed.). ***Indian Painting Today 1981.*** Bombay: JAG, 1981.
---. ***Indian Drawing Today 1987***. Bombay: JAG, 1987.
Chaudhuri, D N (Ed.). ***Jamini Roy: Seminar Papers: In the Context of Indian Folk Sensibility and His Impact on Modern Art***. New Delhi: LKA, 1992.
Chawla, Rupika. ***Ramachandran Art of the Muralist.*** Bangalore: Sara Kala Yatra and Sistas, 1994.
---. ***Surface and Depth: Indian Artists at Work.*** New Delhi: Viking, 1995.
---. ***Ramachandran: Icons of the Raw Earth.*** ---: Kala Yatra, 1999.
Chowdhury, Jogen and Others (Ed.). ***Art of Bengal Past and Present 1850–2000.*** Calcutta: CIMA, 2001.
Chowdhury, Jogen. ***Flowing Life. Text by Uma Nair***. New Delhi:Vadher Art Gallrery, 2005.

Dalmia, Yashodhara and Others (Ed.). ***Indian Contemporary Art: Post Independence***. New Delhi: VAG, 1977.
Dalmia, Yashodhara. ***Making of Modern Indian Art: The Progressives.*** New Delhi: OUP, 2001.
Dalmia, Yashodhara (Ed.). ***Contemporary Indian Art: Other Realities.*** New Delhi: Marg, 2002.
Das, Sekhar Ramyansu. ***Nandalal Bose and Indian Painting***. Calcutta: Tower, 1958.
Datta, Ella. ***Ganesh Pyne: His Life and Times***. Calcutta: CIMA, 1998.
---. ***Art of A Ramachandran.*** New Delhi: Roli Books, 2000.
De, Aditi. ***Articulations: Voice from Contemporary Indian Visual Art***. New Delhi: Rupa, 2004.
Dey, Bishnu and Irwin, John. ***Jamini Roy.*** Calcutta: ISOA, 1944.
Dutta, Ajit Kumar. ***Jamini Roy. Ed. by Jaya Appasamy***. New Delhi: LKA, 1973.

Furtado, R de L. ***Three Painters: Amrita Sher-Gil, George Keyt and M F Husain***. New Delhi: Dhoomimal Ramchand, 1960.

Gandhi, Ramchandra. ***Svaraj: A Journey with Tyeb Mehta's Shantiniketan Triptych***. New Delhi: VAG, 2002.
Ghose, Arun (Ed.). ***Art of Bengal 1850–1950.*** Calcutta: CMFA, 1997.
Ghose, D C. ***Bibliography of Modern Indian Art. Ed. by K L Kaul.*** New Delhi: LKA, 1980.
Ghosh, Nemai. ***Faces of Indian art: Through the lens of Nemai Ghosh.*** New Delhi: Art Alive Gallery, 2007.
Gill, Gagan. ***Ram Kumar: A Journey Within***. New Delhi: VAG, 1978.
Glenbarra Art Museum. ***Jogen Chowdhury: Enigmatic Visions***. Japan: Glenbarra Art Museum, 2005.
Government College of Art and Craft. ***Art in Art Colleges of West Bengal***. Kolkata: BAAC, 2001.
Guha-Thakurta, Tapati. ***Making of a New Indian Art: Artists, Aesthetics and Nationalism in Bengal: 1850-1920***. Cambridge: OUP, 1992.
Gujral, Satish. ***Satish Gujral: Sculptures.*** New Delhi: Roli Books, 2001.

Hanfi, Shamim. ***Yayati: The Complete Man: A Study based on A Ramachandran's Series of Painting and Sculptures.*** New Delhi: ---, 1986.
Herwitz, Daniel. ***Husain: Drawing, Painting, Water Colour, Graphic, Sculpture, Architecture, Photography, Tapestry.*** Mumbai: Tata Steel, 1988.
Hoskote, Ranjit. ***Sudhir Patwardhan: The Complicit Observer***. Mumbai: Sakshi Gallery Synergy Art Foundation, ---.
---. ***Crafting of Reality: Sudhir Patwardhan.*** Mumbai: The Guild, 2007.
Husain, M F. ***Let History Cut Across ... Without Me.*** Bombay: M F Husain Foundation, 1992.
---. ***Where Art Thou: An Autobiography with Khalid Mohamed. Sketches by M F Husain***. Mumbai: Author, 2002.

Jack Shainman Gallery (Pub.). ***Bharti Kher***. New York: JSG, 2000.
Jakimowicz, Marta. ***Akbar Padamsee: Works On Paper: Critical Boundaries***. Mumbai: Pundole, 2004.
Jakimowicz-Karle, Marta. ***Bikash Bhattacharjee***. Bangalore: Kala Yatra, 1991.
James, Josef. ***Cholamandal: Artists' Village***. Chennai: OUP, ---.
Jamini Roy Birth Centenary Exhibition Committee. ***Art of Jamini Roy: A Centenary Volume***. Calcutta: JRBCEC & BAAC, 1987.
Jhaveri, Amrita. ***Guide to 101 Modern Contemporary Indian Artists***. Mumbai: IBH, 2005.

Kapur, Geeta. ***Contemporary Indian Artists***. New Delhi: Vikas, 1979.
---. ***K G Subramanyan***. New Delhi: LKA, 1987.

---. ***When Was Modernism: Essays on Contemporary Cultural Practice In India***. New Delhi: Tulika, 2001.
Kapur, S Shiva. ***M F Husain. Ed. by S A Krishnan***. New Delhi: LKA, 1961.
Karode, Roobina (Ed.). ***Still-Life: Adaptations in the 20th Century India Art***. New Delhi: Delhi Art Gallery, 2007.
---. ***Ambadas: Sublime Encounters 1965 – 2005.*** New Delhi: Delhi Art Gallery, 2007.
---. ***Haren Das: The End of Toil, Prints (1945-1990)***. New Delhi: Delhi Art Gallery, 2008.
Kaul, Shantiveer. ***Art of G R Santosh.*** New Delhi: Roli Books, 2000.
Khanna, Balraj and Kurtha, Aziz. ***Art of Modern India.*** London: Thames and Hudson, 1988.
Khanna, Krishen. ***J Swaminathan. Ed. by Amit Mukhopadhyay***. New Delhi: LKA, 1995.
Khanna, Krishen and Others. ***Krishen Khanna: Images in My Time***. Ahmedabad: Mapin, 2004.
Kowshik, Dinkar. ***Nandalal Bose: The Doyen of Indian Art***. New Delhi: NBT, 1985.
Krishnamachari, Bose. ***De Curating: Indian Contemporary Artists***. Mumbai: Spenta, 2003.
Kumar Gallery (Pub.). ***Celebration 2008.*** New Delhi: Kumar Gallery, 2008.
Kurtha, Aziz. ***Francis Newton Souza 1924–2002: Bridging Western and Indian Modern Art***. Ahmedabad: Mapin, 2006.

Lal, Lakshmi. ***My Brush with Art: An Anthology of Contemporary Indian Art.*** New Delhi: Rupa, 2004.
Lath, Mukund. ***Ardha Kathanaka: Half a Tale. Ill. by Ganesh Pyne***. New Delhi: Rupa, 2005.
Leyden, Von R. ***K H Ara. Ed. by Jaya Appasamy***. New Delhi: LKA, 1965.
Losty, J P. ***Indian Paintings in the British Library***. Bombay: LKA, 1986.
Lynton, Norbert. ***Krishen Khanna: Chola Migrations***. Ahmedabad: Mapin, 2007.

Mago, Pran Nath. ***Contemporary Art in India: A Perspective.*** New Delhi: NBT, 2001.
Majumder, Manasij (Ed.). ***Treasure Trove: Contemporary Indian Art from the Private Collections of Basanta Kumar Birla, Sarala Birla, Jayashree Mohta and Manjushree Khaitan.*** Kolkata: BAAC, 2001.
Majumder, Manasij. ***Close to Events Works of Bikash Bhattacharjee.*** New Delhi: Niyogi Books, 2007.
Malik, Keshav (For.). ***Spirit Set Free***. New Delhi: Kumar Gallery, 2005.
Mazumdar, Nirode (Int.). ***Drawings by Fourteen Contemporary Artists of Bengal Calcutta.*** Calcutta: Priti Mukherjee & Bhawani Mullick, 1970.
Mitter, Partha. ***Art and Nationalism in Colonial India 1850–1922: Occidental Orientations***. New York: CUP, 1994.
---. ***Triumph of Modernism: India's Artists and the Avant-Grade, 1922–1947***. New Delhi: Oxford University Press, 2007.
Mookerjee, Ajit. ***Biren De. Ed. by Amit Mukhopadhyay***. New Delhi: LKA, 1985.
---. ***Modern Art in India***. Calcutta: Oxford Book, ---.
Mukherjee, Rudrangshu (Ed.). ***Art of Bengal: A Vision Defined 1955–1975***. Kolkata: CIMA, 1975.
Mukhopadhyay Amit. ***Satish Gujral: Selected Works 1947–2000***. New Delhi: LKA, 2000.
Mullins, Edwin. ***Souza.*** London: Anthony Blond, 1961.

Nadkarni, Dnyaneshwar. ***Gaitonde. Ed. by R L Bartholomew***. New Delhi: LKA, 1983.
---. ***Husain: Riding the Lightning***. Bombay: Popular, 2000.
Naqvi, Akbar. ***Image and Identity: Fifty Years of Painting and Sculpture in Pakistan.*** Karachi: OUP, 1998.
Padamsee, Akbar. ***Syzygy: Programme For a Film Akbar Padamsee Jawaharlal Nehru Fellowship Project 1969–1970.*** ---: ---, ---.
Pal, Ila. ***Beyond the Canvas: An Unfinished Portrait of M F Husain.*** New Delhi: Indus, 1994.
Panikkar, Shivaji K. ***Creative Process***. Bombay: Guild, 1999.
Parekh, Jayantilal. ***Indian Renaissance, Pioneering Work of Shri Nandalal Bose: A Peprspective On Culture.*** Pondicherry: Pondicherry University, 1885.
Parimoo, Ratan. ***Studies in Modern Indian Art: A Collection of Essays***. New Delhi: Books India, 1975.
Patel, Gieve. ***Poetry with Young People***. New Delhi: Sahitya Akademi, 2007
Peerbhoy, Ayaz S (Presented). ***Husain Letters***. Bombay: Asper Gallery, ---.
Peerbhoy, Ayaz S. ***Paintings of Husain***. Bombay: Thacker, 1955.
Puri, Ina. ***Manjit Bawa: In His Own Words.*** New Delhi: Roli Books, 2000.

Raghuvanshi, Alka. ***Moment in Time: With Legends of Indian Arts***. New Delhi: PD-MIB-GOI, 1996.
---. ***Pathfinders: Artists of One World***. New Delhi: Wisdom Tree, 2002.
Raman, A S. ***Southern Accent: An Introduction to the Art and Artists of Tamil Nadu***. Madras: Tamil Nadir Ovia Nunkalai Kuzhu, 2000.
Raman, A S (Int.). ***Sailoz Mookherjea: 9 Colour Plates and 30 Monochromes***. New Delhi: Dhoomi Mal, ---.
Rao, Ramchandra P R. ***Contemporary Indian Art.*** Hyderabad: The Author, 1969.
Ray, Pranabranjan. ***25 Years of Contemporary India Art 1960–1985.*** Calcutta: Society of Contemporary Artists, 1975.
Royal Academy of Arts. ***Contemporary Indian Art: An Exhibition of the Festival of India 1982***. London: Indian Advisory Committee, Festival of India, 1982.

Sachdev, Nicholai (Cu.). ***Sir J J School of Art: Sesquicentennial Celeberation 1957–2007.*** Mumbai: JJites Association, 2007.
Sadwelkar, Baburao. ***Story of a Hundred Years: The Bombay Art Society 1888–1988***. Bombay: Bombay Art Society, 1975.
Sarkar Shiladitya. ***Thirst of a Minstrel: The Life and Times of Ganesh Pyne***. New Delhi: Rupa, 1998.
Sarkar, Rakhi. ***Trends and Images.*** Calcutta: CIMA, 2005.
Satchidanandamurthy, K (Ed.). ***Divine Peacock: Understanding Contemporary India***. New Delhi: Indian Council for Cultural Relations, 1995.
Seid, Betty. ***New Narratives: New Contemporary Art from India.*** Ahmedabad: Mapin, 2007.
Sen, Geeti. ***S H Raza. Ed. by Amit Mukhopadhyay***. New Delhi: LKA, 1990.
---. ***Image and Imagination: Five Contemporary Artists in India***. Ahmedabad: Mapin, 1996.
Sengupta, Kajal and Sen, Sohini (Eds.). ***Album: 1960–1991: Society of Contemporary Artists Calcutta***. Calcutta: SCA, 1991.
Shamlal. ***Padamsee.*** ---:---, 1961.
Shamlal. ***Ram Kumar. Ed. by Jaya Appasamy.*** New Delhi: LKA, 1968.
Sheikh, Gulam Mohammed. ***New Contemporaries***. Bombay: Marg, 1976.
Sheikh, Gulammohammed (Ed.). ***Contemporary Art in Baroda***. New Delhi: Tulika, 1997.
Siddiqui, Rashda. ***In Conversation with Husain Paintings.*** New Delhi: Books Today, 2001.
Sinha, Gayatri. ***Krishen Khanna: A Critical Biography.*** New Delhi: VAG, 2001.
---. ***Satish Gujral: Drawings and Collages.*** New Delhi: Roli Books, 2001.
---. (Ed.). ***Indian Art: An Overview***. New Delhi: Rupa, 2003.
---. ***Jiva/Life: Contemporary Indian Painting***. Singapore: Bodhi Art, 2004.
---. ***Art of Adimoolam***. New Delhi: Mapin, 2005.
Sinha, Gayatri and Others. ***Satish Gujral: An Artography***. New Delhi: Roli Books, 2006.
Sinha, Modhurima. ***Call of the Real: Contemporary Indian Artists from Bengal***. Ahmedabad: Mapin, 2003.
Sircar, Anjali. ***L Munuswamy. Ed. by Amit Mukhopadhyay***. New Delhi: LKA, 1985.

Siva Kumar, R. ***Ramachandran: A Retrospective. Vol. 1.*** New Delhi: NGMA, 2004.
---. ***Ramachandran: A Retrospective. Vol. 2.*** New Delhi: NGMA, 2004.
Souza, F N. ***Words and Lines***. London: Villiers, 1959.
Subramanyan, K G. ***Living Tradition: Perspectives on Modern Indian Art.*** Calcutta: Seagull, 1987.

Tagore, Abanindranath. ***Some Notes on Indian Artistic Anatomy and Sadanga or the Six Limbs of Painting. Illustrated By Nandalal Bose and K Venkatappa.*** Calcutta: ISOA, 1968.
Thacker, Manu and Venkatachalam, G. ***Present Day Painters of India.*** Bombay: Shantaram Lane, 1950.
Tharoor, Shashi. ***Kerala God's Own Country. Paintings by M F Husain.*** New Delhi: Books Today, 2003.
Tuli, Neville. ***'Flamed–Mosaic: Indian Contemporary Painting.'*** New Delhi: HEART and Mapin, 1997 [International Edition. New York: Harry N Abrams, 1998].

Vadehra Art Gallery. ***Indian Ink: Letter from India 1953–61 by Maratha Mckee Keehn and the Keehn Collection of Modern Indian Art.*** New Delhi: VAG, 2000.
---. ***M F Husain Turns 88: He Takes to Oils on Canvas Paints 88 Works in Four Cities: Mumbai, Delhi, Kolkata and Paris.*** New Delhi: VAG, 2003.
---. ***Tyeb Mehta: Ideas Images Exchanges***. New Delhi: VAG, 2005.
Vajpeyi, Ashok. ***Seven Contemporary Indian Artists.*** New Delhi: Bookwise India, 2003.
---. ***Life in Art Raza***. New Delhi: Art Alive Gallery, 2007.
Vasudev, Uma. ***Satish Gujral. Ed. by S A Krishnan***. New Delhi: LKA, 1970.
---. ***Satish Gujral: Where the Silence Speak: Paintings.*** New Delhi: Roli Books, 2001.
Venkatachalam, G. ***Contemporary Indian Painters***. Bombay: Nalanda, 1927.

Journals and Magazines

Adajania, Nancy. 'Atul Dodiya: Theatre of the Mind.' *The Art India, Vol.1(4), January–*
Alkazi, E (Ed.). 'Catalogue Session: M F Husain.' *Art Heritage, Vol.1, 1978–1979.* pp.62–63.
---. 'Akbar Padamsee.' *Art Heritage, Vol.5, 1985–1986.* pp.84–88.
---. 'M F Husain: Mahabharata series.' *Art Heritage, Vol.9, 1989–1990.* pp.86–87.
---. 'Krishen Khanna: Beyond the Bandwalla's Cacophony: A Non-Committal Statement by the Artist.' *Art Heritage, Vol.10, 1990–1991.* p.44.
Alkazi, E. 'Gujral Speaks.' *Art Heritage, Vol.6, 1986–1987.* pp.50–61.
---. 'Souza's Seasons in Hell.' *Art Heritage, Vol.6, 1986–1987.* pp.74–93.
Amrita. 'Jamini Roy.' *Lalit Kala Contemporary, Vol.2, December,1964.* pp.15–26.
Anand, Mulk Raj(Ed.). 'Some Contemporary Artists: N S Bendre; S Chavda; K K Hebbar; K H Ara; S K Bakre; S Choudhuri and M F Hussain.' *Marg, Vol.4(3), June,1950.* pp.34–38.
---. 'Seven Contemporary Artists: Manishi Dey; Pradosh Das Gupta; Sudhir Khastgir; H A Gade; Gopal Ghose; Ramkinkar Baij and Sailoz Mookherjea.' *Marg, Vol.5(1), December,1951.* pp.34–47.
---. 'Seven Contemporary Artists: Amrita Sher-Gil; Svetoslav Roerich; Rasiklal D Raval; Amar Nath Sehgal; Dhanraj Bhagat; Akbar Padamsee and Satish Gujral.' *Marg, Vol.6(1), December,1952.* pp.28 –41 .
Anand, Mulk Raj (Ed.). 'Three Contemporaries (Abroad): George Keyt; Akbar Padamsee and Chintamoni Kar.' *Marg, Vol.7(3), June,1954.* pp.37–47.
---. 'Painting Under the Sikhs.' *Marg, Vol.7(2), March,1954.* pp.23–31.
---. 'Contemporaries:Triloke Kaul; S N Butt; G R Santosh and P N Kachru.' *Marg, Vol.8(2), March,1955.* pp.101–111.
---. 'Painting and Sculpture: Amrita Sher-Gil; K C Aryan; Dhanraj Bhagat; Satish Gujral; Har Kishan Lal; Krishan Khanna; Kanwal Krishna; Ram Kumar; Prannath Mago; Prashar; Bhabesh Sanyal; Sobha Singh and Thakur Singh.' *Marg, Vol.10(2), March,1957.* pp.59–74.
Appasamy, Jaya. 'Some Contemporary Painters in Delhi: K S Kulkarni; B Sanyal; Kanwal Krishna; Biren De; Dinkar Kowshik; Ram Kumar; K C Aryan; Avinash Chandra and Prannath Mago.' *Marg, Vol.7(4), September,1954.* pp.47–62.
---. 'Three Retrospective Exhibitions: Husain.' *Lalit Kala Contemporary, Vol.10, September,1969.* pp.29–30.
---. 'Two Artists of Distinction: Bikash Bhattacharjee and Sarbari Roychowdhury'. *Art Heritage, Vol.1, 1978–1979.* pp.21–26.
Arakkal, Yusuf. 'My Muse and I: The Artist Talks about the Seven Masters who have Inspired and Influenced Him'. (Baij, Ramkinkar; Michelangelo; Husain, M F; Souza, F N; Kollwitz, Kathe; Van Gogh, Vincent; Picasso, Pablo) *Swagat, Vol.28(1), January, 2007.* pp.92-98.

Bajpai, Neha S. 'Forgers Canvas'. (Raza, S H; Hore, Somnath). *Week. Vol.27 (12),* 15 February 2009. pp.64-65.
Bartholomew, Richard. 'Abstract Principle in the Paintings of Ram Kumar.' *Lalit Kala Contemporary, Vol.19&20, April-September,1975.* pp.9–14.
---. 'Landscape as Vision: Ram Kumar.' *Art Heritage, Vol.4, 1984–1985.* pp.97–109.
---. 'Ram Kumar: The Early Years.' *Art Heritage, Vol.4, 1984–1985.* pp.84–91.
---. 'Three worlds of Satish Gujral.' *Art Heritage, Vol.6, 1986–1987.* pp.62–73.
Bhatnagar, Manjari. 'Courting Controversy yet Again – M F Husain'. *Society, Vol.29(2), December, 2007.* pp.58-60.
---. 'Is India Responsible for M F Husain's Destruction?' *Society, Vol.28(10), August, 2007.* p.34–42.
---. 'Travails of an Art Legend'.(Raza, S H). *Society. January, 2008.* pp.124-127.

Chuganee, Bhakti. 'Collectors: A Passion for Art Runs like a Common Thread among India's Top Collectors'. (Bawa, Manjit; Bendre, N S; Bhattacharjee, Bikash; Bhattacharya, Sanjay; Bose, Krishnamachari;Bose, Nandlal; Burman, Shakti; Chowdhury, Jogen; Das, Arup; Dodiya, Atul; Goud, Laxma; Hore, Somnath; Husain, M F; Kanodia, Naina; Khakkar, Bhupen; Mehta, Tyeb; Nair, Surendran; Padamsee, Akbar; Padwal, Sunil; Prabha, B; Pyne, Ganesh; Ramkumar; Raza, S H; Roy, Jamini; Sabavala, Jehangir; Sen, Paritosh; Shreshta, Laxman; Singh, Arpita; Sud, Anupam; Sundaram, Vivan; Tagore, Abanindranath; Tagore, Gyanendranath; Tagore, Rabindranath; Thozur, Vasundhar; Upadhyaya, Hema; Verma, Raja Ravi). *Business India. 09 March, 2008.* pp.102-107.

Dalmia, Yashodhara. 'Tyeb Mehta: Beyond Narrative Painting: An Interview with Yashodhara Dalmia.' *Art Heritage, Vol.9, 1989–1990.* pp.76–85.
---. 'Life and Times of Ganesh Pyne. '*Lalit Kala Contemporary, Vol.44, June, 2001.* pp.41–42.
---. 'Masters of the Grotesque: For the First Time, Indian and European Greats Exhibit Together.' (Bacon, Francis; Freud, Lucian; Mehta, Tyeb; *Souza, F N) Outlook, Vol.32(36), 10 September, 2007.* pp.60-61.
Datta, Ella. 'Akbar Padamsee: The Spirit of Order.' *Art Heritage, Vol.8, 1988–1989.* pp.33–56.
Datta, Pronoti. 'Alt Space'. (Patwardhan, Sudhir). *Time Out Mumbai,* Vol.(4)8, 14 December, 2007. p.30.
Dutt, Nirupama. 'But for Art: The Progressive Artists Group gave Art an Identity in Independent India'. (Gade, H A; Raza, S H; Souza, F N; Husain, M F; Mehta, Tyeb; Gaitonde, V S; Ara, K H) *Swagat, Vol.(28)6, June, 2007.* pp.86-94.
Dutta, Santo. 'Visitations: Obsessive Imagery in the Works of Some Modern Indian Painters (Jogen Chowdhury; K C S Paniker).' *Art Heritage, Vol.2, 1980–1981.* pp.83–89.

Editor. 'Some Respite'. (Husain, M F.). *Business India. 01 June, 2008.* p.146.
---. 'Idylls in Memoriam'. (Bawa, Manjit). *Outlook. Vol.49 (3), 26 January 2009.* p.76.
Gaitonde, V S. 'I Keep Painting in My Head and the Process Will Go on....' *The Art India, Vol.1(4), January–February, 2000.* pp.20–21.
Gaur, Umesh and Sinha, Gayatri. 'American Collectors of Contemporary Indian Art in the Northeast'. (Husain, M F; Gaitonde, V S; Khanna, Krishen; Bendre, N S; Souza, F N; Ram Kumar; Reddy, Ravinder; Mehta, Tyeb). *Orientations, Vol.33(6), June, 2002.* pp.31-36.
Geeta Doctor. 'Colonial Canavas'. (Roy, Jamini; Bose, Nandalal; Tagore, Rabindranath; Baij, Ramkinkar; Mukhopadhyaya, Benodebehari; Roy Chowdhury, D.B). *India Today, Vol.(32)49, 10 December, 2007.* p.85.

Gokhale, Shanta. 'Drawing the Line: Censorship and the Arts: M F Husain; Akbar Padamsee; F N Souza; Bhupen Khakhar and Arpita Singh.' *The Art India, Vol.1(4), September,1996.*
Goud, Laxma. 'Catalogue Session: Laxma Goud.' *Art Heritage, Vol.1, 1978–1979.* pp.59–61.

Hoskote, Ranjit. 'Akbar Padamsee: Between the Hieratic and the Human.' *Art Heritage, Vol.11, 1991–1992.* pp.131–146.
---. 'Life and Legend of Maqbool Fida Husain.' *International Gallerie: A Journey of Idea, Vol.3(1), 2000.* pp.4–25.
Indrasimhan, Lakshmi. 'Very Hungry Collaboration'. (Gupta, Subodh; Kher, Bharti). *Tehelka.* Vol.5 (26), 29-05 July, 2008. pp.48-51.

Kapur, Geeta, 'Six Indian Painters: Rabindranath Tagore; Jamini Roy; Amrita Sher-Gil; M F Husain; K G Subramanyan and Bhupen Khakhar'. *Marg, Vol. 35(4), September,1983.* pp.59–64.

Karunakar, Pria. 'V S Gaitonde.' *Lalit Kala Contemporary, Vol.19&20, April-September,1975.* pp.15–17.
Khanna, K. 'Studies in Development of M F Husain.' *Marg, Vol.6(2), March,1952.* pp.56–59.
Kher, Bharti. 'Histories in the Making.' *Art Heritage, Vol.14, 1994–1995.* pp.81–88.
Kilachand, Tara. 'Economic of Being Subodh Gupta'. (Gupta, Subodh; Kher, Bharti). *Mint Lounge,* Vol.6 (34). 06 September, 2008. pp.1, 12-14.
Kotin, Veena. 'Raza Revisited.' *The Art India, Vol.1(1), October, 2004.* pp.46–48.
Kowshik, Dinkar. 'Somnath Hore: Wounds in Bronze.' *Art Heritage, Vol.6, 1986–1987.* pp.110–118.
Krishnan, S A. 'Sudhi Ranjan Bhusan.' *Lalit Kala Contemporary, Vol.21, April,1976.* p.20.
---. 'Three Retrospective Exhibitions: M F Husain.' *Lalit Kala Contemporary, Vol.27, April,1979.* pp.20–22.
Kumar, Vinod. 'F N Souza: The Works of Forties.' *Lalit Kala Contemporary, Vol.32, April,1985.* pp.42–43.

Lechner, Georg. Art–East and West: Ernst Fuchs; S H Raza; Bikash Bhattacharjee; Mark Prent; Francis Newton Souza; Peter Nagel; Pillo Pochkhanawala; Balan Nambiar; G R Santosh; Jeram Patel; Wolfgang Laib; Peter Kinley; Claude Lagoutte and Manjit Bawa.' *Marg, Vol.38(4), September,1986.* pp.7–85.
Leyden, R V. 'Studies in Development of K H Ara.' *Marg, Vol.6(2), March,1952.* pp.52–55.
Livingstone, Robert. 'Reinhard Behrens: Forays into Naboland.' *Art Heritage, Vol.9, 1989–1990.* pp.12–16.

Malik, Keshav. 'Jogen Choudhury.' *Lalit Kala Contemporary, Vol.22, September,1976.* pp.21–22.
Marwah, Mala. 'Francis Newton Souza: Expression in Style.' *Lalit Kala Contemporary, Vol.22, September,1976.* pp.4–6.
---. 'Drawing and Liner Expression: Six Contemporary Artists: M F Husain, Jeram Patel, A Ramachandran, Laxma Goud, F N Souza, Bikash Bhattacharjee'. *Art Heritage, Vol.1, 1978–1979.* pp.12–15 .
Mohamedbhai, Tasneem. 'Affair of the Heart: Ten Art Collectors Reveal Their Passion for the World of Art'. (Bawa, Manjit;Bhattacharjee, Bikash;Broota, Rameshwar;Das, jatin;Dodiya, Anju;Dodiya, Atul;Goud, Laxma;Gupta, Subodh;Husain, M F;Khakkar, Bhupen;Khanna, Krishen;Mehta, Tyeb;Menon, Anjolie Ela;Padamsee, Akbar;Pyne, Ganesh;Ram Kumar;Ramanujam, K;Raza, S H;Roy, Jamini;Sabavala, Jehangir;Sheikh, Nilima;Singh, Arpita;Souza, F N;Upadhyay, Hema;Varma, Raja Ravi). *Beautiful People.Vol.3 (4),* January – February 2009. pp.54-65.
Mukherjee, Benode Behari. 'Abanindranath and His Tradition: Preface: Abanindranath Tagore; Nandlal Bose; Asit Kumar Haldar; Gaganendranath Tagore; K Venkatappa; Sailendranath Dey; Kshitindranath Majumdar and Samarendranath Gupta.' *Lalit Kala Contemporary, Vol.1, June, 1962.* pp.23–68.
Mukhopadhyay, Amit. 'Nandalal Bose: The Helmsman.' *Lalit Kala Contemporary, Vol.38, March,1993.* pp.64–69.
Nagrath, Sumati. 'Business of Art'. (Souza, F N; Natesan, Shibu; Husain, M F; Mehta, Tyeb; Raza, S H; Ram Kumar; Souza, F N; Gaitonde, V S; Dodiya, Atul; Broota, Rameshwar; Pyne, Ganesh; Singh, Arpita; Chowdhury, Jogen; Gupta, Subodh; Santosh, T V; Natesan, Shibu; Upadhyay, Chintan; Kallat, Jitish; Balasubramanium, A; Panda, Jagannath). *Businessworld, Vol.27(6), 19 November, 2007.* pp.34-41.
Padamsee, Akbar. 'Akbar Padamsee.' *Art Heritage, Vol.4, 1984–1985.* pp.75–78.

Pal, Deepanjana. 'Art of Space'. (Kallat, Jitish; Komu, Riyas; Gupta, Shilpa; Shetty, Sudarshan). *Time Out Mumbai, Vol.(4)8, 14 December, 2007*. pp.24-28.
---. 'Guide to Buying Art'. (Dodiya, Atul; Gupta, Subodh; Hashmi, Zarina; Husain, M F ; Kher, Bharti; Krishnamachari, Bose; Mehta, Tyeb; Padamsee, Akbar; Santosh, T V; Bari Kumar; Sher-Gil, Amrita; Souza, F N). *Time Out Mumbai. Vol. 4 (18), 02-15 May, 2008*. pp.22-35.
---. 'M F Husain Artist'. (Husain, M F; Raza, S H; Souza, F N). *Time Out Mumbai*, Vol.5 (2), 19-02 October, 2008. p.26.
Parimoo, Ratan. 'Paintings and Sketches of Nandalal Bose.' *Marg, Vol.36(2), March,1984*. pp.5–20.
Pinto, Jerry. 'Art of Sudhir Patwardhan'. (Patwardhan, Sudhir). *Man's World, Vol.(8)9, December 2007*. pp.126-128.

Rain. 'Thirty Three Contemporary Artists.'*International Gallerie: A Journey of Idea, Vol.6(1), 2003*. pp.13–71.
Rajadhayaksha, Asish. 'Sudhir Patwardhan: The Redemption of the Physical.' *Art Heritage, Vol.9, 1989–1990*. pp.4–11.
Ram Kumar. 'Impressions of Varnasi: Wax and Ink Painting by Ram Kumar.' *Art Heritage, Vol.4, 1984–1985*. pp.92–93.
Ramachandran, A. 'Notes from the Underground.' *Art Heritage, Vol.6, 1986–1987*. pp.23–33.
Rao, P R Ramachandra. 'Modern Indian Painting: N S Bendre; K H Ara; M F Husain; M A Rahman Chugtai; Jamini Roy and Nandalal Bose and Madhav Satwalkar: Book Review.' *Marg, Vol.7(1), December,1953*. pp.40–44.

Ravindran, Shruti. 'Life's Frescoes: Celebrating a Master's Astonishing Versatility'.(Bose, Nandalal). *Outlook. Vol.49 (7)*, 23 February 2009. p.69.

Sardesai, Abhay. 'Cinema is Really a Medium for a Painter: Interview with M F Husain.' *The Art India, Vol.9(2), October, 2004*. pp.62–63.
Sarin, Rekha. 'Satish Gujral: Painter, Muralist, Sculptor et al.' *Swagat, April, 1991*. pp.12–18.
Sarkar, Sandip. 'Jamini Roy.' *Art & Deal, Vol.1(1), November–December, 1998*. pp.12–14.
Sen, Geeti. 'Gaja Gamini: The Act of Transformation: M F Husain.' *The Art India, Vol.4(4), October,1999*. pp.54–58.
Shahani, Roshan. 'Paris, Mon Amour: S H Raza Studio.' *The Art India, Vol.9(1), October, 2004*. pp.54–56.
Shekhar, Ratana Rao. 'Heart of Darkness: Talks to K Laxma Goud.' *The Art India, Vol.3(3), June,1998*. pp.61–63.
Subramanyan, K G. 'Drawings of Nandalal Bose.' *Art Heritage, Vol.2, 1980–1981*. pp.55–72.
Suhrawardy, Shahid. 'Jamini Roy.' *Marg, Vol.2(1), December,1947*. pp.66–78.
Sundaram, Vivan. 'Amrita Sher-Gil: Life and Work.' *Marg, Vol.25(2), March,1972*. pp.5–22.
Swaminathan, J Liquid and Sparkling: The Art of Manjit Bawa.' *Swagat, December,1993*. pp.102–109.

Thayil, Keet. 'Smell of Words and Turpentine: A Brown Nude for Akbar Padamsee.' *The Art India, Vol.6(2), October, 2001*. p.73.
Tuli, Neville. 'Bombay's Contribution to Indian Contemporary Painting.' *The Taj Magazine, Vol.25(1), July–September,1996*. pp.18–31.
---. 'Art of Creating Wealth'. (Broota, Rameshwar; Gupta, Subodh; Mehta, Tyeb; Parthan, Baiju; Ramkumar; Souza, F N; Swaminathan, J). *Outlook Profit. 16 May, 2008*. pp.70-71.
Yadav, R S. 'Ram Kumar at Vadehra.' *The Art India, Vol.1(4), January–February, 2000*. pp.40–41.

Group Exhibiton Catalogue

Aakriti Art Gallery. *Collection 2005*. Kolkata: AAG, 2005. p.30.
---. *Shilpakriti: Sculptural Show*. Kolkata: AAG, 12-27 August 2006. p.32.
---. *Folk in Modern*. Kolkata: AAG, 02-17 September 2006. p.24
---. *On Their Own: An Exhibition of Abstract Paintings: A Tribute to Badhan Das*. Kolkata: AAG, 20–31 January 2007. p.24.
---. *Indigenous Modernity Various Trends: An Exhibition of Paintings by Senior Artists of West Bengal*. Kolkata: AAG, 18-28 February 2007. p.50.
---. *Indian Surrealism*. Kolkata: AAG, 20 December 2007–05 January 2008. p.86.
---. *Empty And Full. Text by Prayag Shukla*. Kolkata: AAG, 09 – 20 September 2008. p.28.
Academy of Fine Arts. *Nineteenth Annual Exhibition*. Calcutta: AFA, 1954. p.40
---. *Twentysixth Annual Exhibition*. Calcutta: AFA, 16 December 1961-15 January 1962. p.62.
---. *Paintings of Jamini Roy*. Calcutta: AFA, 1972. p.22.
---. *Paintings of Jamini Roy*. Calcutta: AFA, 1982. p.14.
Academy of Visual Media. *2002 India Korea Contemporary Art Exhibition*. New Delhi: AVM, 2002. p.50.
Akar Prakar. *Tempera*. Kolkata: AP, 06-11 August 2005. p.20.
---. *Synchrome*. Kolkata: AP, 06-15 November 2005. p.32.
---. *Synchrome 3*. Kolkata: AP, 16-28 October 2006. p.58.
---. *Nirmiti*. Kolkata: AP, 13-28 November 2006. p.78.
---. *Art in Itself: How India's South Engages*. Kolkata: AP, 24 February – 3 March 2007. p.24.
---. *Amurta*. Kolkata: AP, 17-29 September 2007. p.52.
---. *3 Masters, Briefly. Text by Pranabranjan Ray*. Kolkata: AP, 14 – 23 October 2008. p.40.
All India Fine Arts and Crafts Society. *2nd International Contemporary Art Exhibition*. New Delhi: AIFACS, 05 May 1953. p.58.
---. *5th International Contemporary Art Exhibition*. New Delhi: IFACS, 19 December 1965. p.64.
---. *42nd All India Art Exhibition*. New Delhi: AIFACS, 19 November 1972. p.20.
---. *58th Annual All India Art Exhibition*. New Delhi: AIFACS, 21 February 1986. p.34.
---. *Drawing 86: An All India Exhibition of Drawing*. New Delhi: AIFACS, 06-12 November; Chandigarh: GCA, 21 Noveber-04 December 1986. p.52.
---. *4th All India Traditional Art Exhibition and 6th All India Water Colour Exhibition*. New Delhi: AIFACS, 24 February-03 March 1987 (AIFACS - New Delhi); 10-20 March 1987. p.35.
---. *Tenth International Contemporary Art Exhibition and Third International Graphic Art Exhibition*. New Delhi: AIFACS, 1988. p.80.
---. *Korea Indo Art 1995*. New Delhi: AIFACS, 26 June-05 July 1995. p.60.
---. *AIFACS Regional Centre Inaugural Art Exhibition*. New Delhi: AIFACS, 25 November-17 December 1995. p.71.
Alliance Française. *Paintings and Drawings by Sultan Ali. Text by Didier Maule and J Sultan Ali*. Madras: AF, 1986.
Allure Art Gallery. *Dream Realised: Contemporary Indian Art Show*. Baroda: AAG, 03-17 May 2008. p.96.
---. *Ritu*. New Delhi: AAG, 08-17 January 2005. p.55.
---. *Configurations*. New Delhi: AAG, 17-26 August 2005. p.20.
---. *Strangeness*. Kolkata: AAG, January 2006. p.20.
Anthony Blond Ltd. *Souza. Text by Edwin Mullins*. London: ABL, 1962. p.18.
Apparao Galleries. *Indian Beast*. Madras: AG, 1997. p.10.
---. *Search*. Madras: AG, 1997. p.10.
---. *Ganesha Paintings*. Chennai: AG, 1998. p.10.
---. *CIAF 99: Contemporary Indian Art Fair 1999. Cu. by Sharan Apparao*. New Delhi: AG, 06 – 18 January 1999. p.96.
---. *Cinema Still*. Madras: AG, 2002. p.15.
---. *Finding At The Centre Margins*. Madras: AG, 2002. p.10.

---. *Navarasaa*. Madras: AG, 2002. p.20.
---. *Ruminations*. Madras: AG, 2004. p.33.
Arks Gallery. *Recent Works by Ram Kumar. Text by Ranjit Hoskote*. London: AG, 1996. p.42.
Art Alive Gallery. *Tatva: The Elements Showcasing Six Indian Masters*. New Delhi: AAG, 11-17 June 2006; London: SAFA, 02 June 2006. p.52.
---. *Swasti Roop: Expressions in Abstraction by Raza Foundation Awardees*. New Delhi: AAG, 23 February - 24 March 2007. p.64.
Art and Soul. *Journey 2: A Charity Show for Passages*. Mumbai: AS, 2006. p.118.
---. *Mumbai Metronomes: Mumbai Artists Define the Limits*. Mumbai: AS, 23 July 2007. p.50.
Art for Ashraya. *Art for Ashraya*. Bangalore: AA, 12-17 February 1997. p.24.
Art Galleries Association. *Contemporary Asian Art Fair*. Singapore: AGA, 11-15 October 2002. p.128.
Art Gallery of New South Wales. *India Songs: Multiple Streams in Contemporary Indian Art*. Sydney: AGNSW, 01 April-09 May 1993. p.55.
Art Heritage. *Catalog 1981-82. Des. by E Alkazi and Suhas Nimblakar*. New Delhi: AH, 1980.
Art Heritage. *Sultan Ali: Paintings*. New Delhi: AH, 1997. p.48.
Art Indus. *Art Indus*. New Delhi: AI, 11-30 September 1997. p.18.
---. *Tribute to Mother Teresa: Exhibition of Paintings and Sculptures*. New Delhi: AI, 14-29 November 1997. p.16.
---. *Arts in Art*. New Delhi: Shridharani Gallery, 24-31 October 2006. p.58.
Art Konsult. *Magnetic Forms*. New Delhi: AK, 16 August-03 September 1997. p.24.
---. *Joie de Vivre*. New Delhi: AK, 06-12 December 2005. p.75.
---. *Mark, Eich and Print*. New Delhi: AK, 19 December 2006-10 January 2007. p.52.
Art Mill (The). *Art Mill*. Mumbai: TAM, 06-20 May; London: BSG, 15-24 June 2006. p.25.
Art Motif. *Pastel*. New Delhi: AM, 06 October 1996. p.68.
---. Contemporary Indian Art. New Delhi: AM, 2005. p.40.
---. *Pastles: Contemporary Indian Art*. New Delhi: AM, 06-13 January 2008. p.50.
Art Musings. *Exhibition of Paintings by M F Husain, S H Raza, Anjolie Ela Menon, Paresh Maity*. Mumbai: AM, 07 December 1999-15 January 2000. p.20.
---. *Exhibition of Paintings*. Mumbai: AM, 07 December 1999-15 January 2000. p.20.
---. *Art Musings: Celebrates Anniversary Return to Eden*. Mumbai: AM, 08-31 January 2001. p.26.
---. *Return to Eden*. Mumbai: AM, 08-31 January 2001. p.20.
---. *Art Musings 2002*. Mumbai: AM, 2002. p.21.
---. *Art Musings: Celebrate Anniversary Master Strokes*. Mumbai: AM, 15 March-08 April 2003. p.26.
---. *Master Strokes*. Mumbai: AM, 2003. 15 March-08 April 2003. p.24.
---. *Art Musings 2004*. Mumbai: MG, 16-22 August; Mumbai: AM, 22-31 August 2004. p.38.
---. *Alchemy*. Mumbai: JAG, 13-19 October; Mumbai: AM, 20-30 October 2005. p.47.
---. *Resonance*. Mumbai: AM, 07-22 February 2005. p.36.
---. *Resonance 2006*. Mumbai: MG, 12-17 December 2006; Mumbai: AM, 19 December 2006-20 January 2007. P.76.
---. *Resonance: In the pause between Phrase and Images – K G Subramanyan, Jogen Chowdhury, Sakti Burman and Anjolie Ela Menon. Text by Ranjit Hoskote* .Mumbai: Museum Gallery, 12–17 December; Art Musings, 19–20 December 2006. p.56.
---. *Collection*. Mumbai: AM, 22 – 30 July 2008. p.24.
Art Today. *Maqbool Fida Husain's Rare Paintings Signed*. New Delhi: AT, 1995. p.26.
---. *River of Art: The Inaugural Delhi Show*. New Delhi: AT, ---. p.35
Artists Centre. *Jubilant Gold: 50 Years of Artists Centre*. Mumbai: AC,15-25 March 2001. p.25.
Arts India. *Kaam*. New York: AI, 02 December 2005-22 January 2006; Palo Alto: AI, 17 February-12 March 2006. p.60.
Arts Trust. *Masters of India Art Show*. Mumbai: AT, 15-22 March 1992. p.14.
---. *Art for God's Sake: Approaches to the Divine*. New Delhi: VAG, 21-26 August 2005. p.24.
Arushi Art Gallery. *Harvest 2002: An Exhibition of Indian Contemporary Art 2002*. New Delhi: AAG, 2002. p.52.
---. *Harvest 2003: An Exhibition of Indian Contemporary Art 2003*. New Delhi: AAG, 2003. p.32.
---. *Indian Old and Contemporary Paintings*. New Delhi: AAG, 03 September-03 October 2003. p.39.
---. *Harvest 2004: Art and Poetry*. New Delhi: AAG, 2004. p.78.
---. *Indian Contemporary Paintings*. New Delhi: AAG, 23 September-23 October 2004. p.34.
---. *Indian Old and Contemporary Paintings*. New Delhi: AAG, 20 March-10 April 2004. p.39.
---. *Harvest 2005: An Exhibition of Indian Contemporary Art*. Mumbai: Rampart Row, 25-26 February; Mumbai: AA, 28 February-15 March 2005. p.45.
---. *Indian Contemporary Paintings*. New Delhi: AAG, 10-20 October 2005. p.52.
---. *Now: Group Exhibition of Paintings*. New Delhi: AAG, 16-27 September 2005. p.26.
Arushi Arts. *Harvest 2007: An Exhibition of Indian Contemporary Art*. New Delhi: TMH, 11 August; New Delhi: AFAL, 13-20 August; New Delhi: AA, 14-31 August 2007 p.147.
Aryan Art Gallery. *Visual Rhapsody: An International Painting Exhibition. Cu by Debasish Chand*. New Delhi & Hong Kong: AAG, 2008. p. 40.
Associated Capsules Worldwide Gallery Art. *Resource Trust 100 Contemporary Indian Artist 2005*. Bombay: Kala Ghoda, 03-04 October 2005. p.36.
Aura Art Gallery. *Aura art show 2008. Cu. by Sethi Harmeet Singh*. Mumbai: AAG, 29 January – 04 February 2008. p.118.

Birla Academy of Art and Culture. *Exhibition of Contemporary Art 1977*. Calcutta: BAAC, 09-30 January 1977. p.10.
---. *Exhibition of Contemporary Art 1980*. Calcutta: BAAC, 09-27 January 1980. p.24.
---. *The Art of Jamini Roy: A Centenary Volume*. Calcutta: BAAC, 1987.
---. *Eight Contemporary Artists*. Calcutta: BAAC, 09-31 January 1987. p.30.
---. *25th Anniversary Exhibition of Calcutta Painters*. Calcutta: BAAC, 01-10 March 1990. p.24.
---. *Golden Tribute To The Artists of Southern India on Our Silver Jubilee*. Calcutta: BAAC, 03-29 November 1992. p.42.
---. *Golden Tribute to the Artists of Eastern India on Our Silver Jubilee*. Calcutta: BAAC, 09-31 January 1992. p.40.
---. *Urban Signals Shifting Images*. Mumbai: BAAC, 25 March-10 April 1996; Calcutta: BAAC, 30 April-19 May 1996. p.46.
---. *Urban Signals Shifting Images – II*. Mumbai: BAAC, 11-25 August 1996. p.20.
---. *24 Contemporary Indian Artists*. Calcutta: BAAC, 05-18 April 1997. p.16.
---. *Kalighat - Drawings Patachitra and Contemporary Indian Artists*. Calcutta: BAAC, 17-18 December 1997. p.20.
---. *Vilas the Idea of Pleasure*. Calcutta: BAAC, 2000. p.34.
---. *Distilations*. Mumbai: BAAC, 17 October-04 November 2000. p.65.
---. *Family Resemblances: Nine Approaches to a Mutable Self*. Mumbai: BAAC, 18-30 March 2000. p.20.
---. *Genesis of Ramkinkar*. Calcutta: BAAC, 22 February-19 March 2000. p.30
---. *Paritosh Sen: Mini Retrospective*. Kolkata: BAAC, 2001. p.28.
Bombay Art Society. *Bombay Art Society: 59th Annual Exhibition 1949–1950*. Bombay: BAS, 1950. p.30.

---. *Bombay Art Society: Sixtyfirst Annual Exhibition 1951–1952.* Bombay: BAS, 1952. p.30.
---. *Bombay Art Society: Sixtythird Annual Exhibition 1953–1954.* Bombay: BAS, 1953. p.40.
---. *Bombay Art Society Centenary Invitees Show 1989.* Bombay: JAG, 12-19 December 1989. p.42.
---. *Story of A Hundred Years: The Bombay Art Society 1888-1988 - The Retrospective Exhibition of Old Masters Associated With The Bombay Art Society. Com. by Baburao Sadwelkar.* Bombay: BAS, 1989. p.34.
Bose Pacia Modern. *Early Masters: Rare Paintings of the Bengal Renaissance.* New York: BPM, 1998. p.30.
---. *Icon: India Contemporary.* New York: BPM, 12 June-31 July 2005. p.71.
---. *114th All India Annual Art Exhibition 2006.* Mumbai: BAS, 2006. p.46.
Bose Pacia. *Gieve Patel and Sudhir Patwardhan.* New York: BP, 19 January – 4 March 2006.

Calcutta Metropolitan Festival of Art. *Art of Bengal 1850–1950. Cu. by Ganesh Haloi and Ed. by Arun Ghosh.* Calcutta: CMFA, 1997. p.112.
Cancer Patients Aid Associations. *Art for Hope - Hope for Cancer: An All India Exhibition of Contemporary Art.* Bangalore: CPAA, 08-09 December 1995. p.30.
---. *Colours of Life: An Art Exhibition for a Cause.* Mumbai: CAG, 16-18 March 2005. p.64.
Center for International Modern Art. *Jogen: Oils and Drawings 1969–96.* Calcutta: CIMA, 1996. p.36.
---. *Chamatkara: Myth and Magic in Indian Art. Cu. by Rakhi Sarkar.* London: Whiteleys Art Gallery, 29 October–15 November, 1996. p.40. (See also WAG)
---. *Husain.* Calcutta: CIMA, 1998. p.20.
---. *Trends and Images. Cu. by Barun Bhattacharjee.* Calcutta: CIMA, 1993. p.26.
---. *Contemporary Miniatures 1994.* Calcutta: CIMA, 17 September-08 October 1994. p.45.
---. *Fantasy.* Calcutta: CIMA, 25 February-12 March 1995. p.80.
---. *Chamatkara: Myth and Magic in Indian Art.* London: WAG, 29 October-15 November 1996. p.144.
Chawla Art Gallery. *Embrace: The Inclusive Art Event.* New Delhi: CAG, 22 April 2005. p.28.
---. *Annual Group Show. Text by Keshav Malik.* New Delhi: CAG, 19 – 30 April 2008. p.110.
Child Relief and You (CRY). *Art for Cry: An Exhibition of Contemporary Indian Art in Aid of Deprived Indian Children.* Bombay: JAG, 30 January–5 February; New Delhi: LKA, 17–23 February 1995. 1995. p.46.
---. *Art for Cry: Contemporary Art Produced to Support CRY's Work with Underprivileged Children and To Commemorate Ten Years of CRY.* Bombay: JAG 1-10 September; Calcutta: BAAC 18–24 September; New Delhi: College of Art 1-8 October; Bangalore: KCKP 17–22 October 1–10,---.
Chitrakoot Art Gallery. *Faces: Paintings and Mixed Media work by Rabin Mondal. Text by J Sultan Ali.* Calcutta: CAG, 1987. p.12.
---. *Homage to Bikash Bhattacharya by His Disciples. Text by Kamalaksha Gangopadhyay.* Kolkata: CAG, 25 December 2006–5 January 2007. p.11.
Chivas Regal. *Experience Chivas Art Alive.* Chivas Regal: CR, 2005. p.54.
Classic Source Gallery. *Rare and Important Paintings.* Mumbai: SAG, 05 September-07 October 1997. p.20.
Classic Source Gallery (The). *Faces and Figures.* Mumbai: TCSG, 27 April 1998. p.40.
CMC Art Gallery. *Jamini Roy.* New Delhi: CMCAG, 1991. p.18.
Crimson - The Art Resource. *Ignition: An Exhibition by 40 Artists.* Mumbai: CAR, 2000. p.30.
Cymroza Art Gallery. *Cymroza Art Gallery: 1991–1992. Ed. by Pheroza J Godrej.* Bombay: CAG,1992. p.90.
---. *Xal Praxis Foundation.* Mumbai: CAG, 04-21 November 1992. p.10.
---. *Paintings and Sculptures by Sixteen Contemporary Artists.* Mumbai: CAG, 08-25 September 1993. p.12.
---. *Cymroza Art Gallery 1993–1994.* Mumbai: CAG, 1994. p.98.
---. *Cymroza Art Gallery: The Silver Jubilee Exhibition.* Mumbai: CAG, 24 October-09 November 1996. p.20.
---. *Cymroza Art Gallery 1996-1997.* Mumbai: CAG, 1997. p.102.
---. *Cymroza Art Gallery: The Silver Jubilee Exhibition–2.* Mumbai: CAG, 11-28 June 1997. p.20.
---. *Exhibition of Paintings and Sculptures Dedicated to Mother Teresa.* Mumbai: CAG, 05-17 October 1998. p.14.
---. *Eye of the South: An Exhibition of Paintings by 26 Artists from South India.* Mumbai: CAG, 09-26 August 2000. p.20.
---. *Architects and Artists.* Mumbai: CAG, 01-15 October 2001. p.18.
---. *Work of Art a Work On Paper. Text by Ranjit Hoskote.* Mumbai: CAG, 4–28 October 2006. p.54.

Delhi Art Gallery. *Group Exhibition 1974.* New Delhi: Rabindra Bhavan, 1974. p.20.
---. *Edge of the Century: An Exhibition of Contemporary Indian Art.* New Delhi: Gallery Mirage, 04-31 January; New Delhi: DAG, 06-29 January; New Delhi: VAG, 07-19 January; New Delhi: NM, 08-28 January; New Delhi: Gallery 42, 09-31 January; New Delhi: British Council, 10-24 January; New Delhi: SSSPAG, 12-27 January; New Delhi: AFAL, 14-25 January; New Delhi: HICC, 15-30 January ; New Delhi: Gallery OM, 16-31 January; New Delhi: AI, 16-25 January; New Delhi: AT, 18-30 January; New Delhi: LTGAG, 20 January-07 February; New Delhi: GRRAF, 21 January-06 February; New Delhi: MMB, 22 January-07 February; New Delhi: AK, 25 January-08 February 1999. p.140.
---. *Face off 1900-1980s: An Exhibition of Indian Old Masters and Moderns.* New Delhi: DAG, 15 April-31 May 2000. p.70.
---. *Changing Images: An Exhibition of 20th Century Indian Art.* New Delhi: DAG, 07-14 August 2001. p.131.
---. *Manifestations I Indian Art in the 20th Century. Ed. by Roobina Karode.* Mumbai: WTC, 12–19 November; New Delhi: DAG, 29 November–13 December, 2003. p.74.
---. *Poetry and Patriotic Fervour. Indian Art Pre-Independence.* New Delhi: DAG, 2003. p.96.
---. *Manifestations II: Indian Art in the 20th Century. Ed. by Roobina Karode.* Mumbai: JAG, 25–31 July; New Delhi: DAG, 9–21 August 2004. p.238
---. *Manifestations III: 100 Artists. Ed. by Roobina Karode.* Mumbai: Nehru Centre, 6-12 April; New Delhi: Rabindra Bhavan, 22–7 April; DAG 30 April–14 May 2005. p.56.
---. *Naked Line: Drawings by 12 Artists*(F N Souza, A Ramachandran, Rabin Mondal, J Sultan Ali, Jai Zharotia, Jeram Patel, Ambadas Khobragad, Himmat Shah, K Laxma Goud, Sunil Das, Chittaprosad Bhatacharya) Curated by Roobina Karode. New Delhi: DAG,2006. p.299.
---. *Pai in Paris Early Works. Cu. by Karode Roobina.* New Delhi: DAG, 27 April – 18 May 2006. p.101.
---. *Frame Figure Field. Text by Roobina Karode.* New Delhi: DAG, 17 October – 20 November 2008. p.92.
---. *Shiksha 2007: A Group Exhibition of Paintings by Indian Contemporary Artists.* New Delhi: DFRT, 16 March 2007. p.191.
Deutsche Bank. *Contemporary art. Text by Kamala Kapoor.* Bombay: DB, 1995. p.56.
Dhoomimal Art Centre. *Creative Endeavours In Small Format. Text by P N Mago.* New Delhi: DAC, 17 January – 11 February 1997. p.10.
---. *Gulam Rasool Santosh. Text by Shantiveer Kaul.* New Delhi: DAC, 1998. p.22.
Dhoomimal Gallery. *Contemporary Indian art: A Journey to the Past, Through the Present, Unto Future. Ed. by Umesh Varma.* New Delhi: DG, 2003. p.64.

---. *Drawing the Essence*. Mumbai: DG, 2005. p.32.
Eastern Zonal Cultural Centre. *Drawings: Friendship' 95. Ed. By Deben Dewan*. Calcutta: EZCC, 1995. p.60.
Emamichisel Art. *Signature: Art Fest 2008*. Kolkata: ECA, 23 April-07 May 2008. p.30.
Fine Art Company. *Legatee Sir J.J. School of Art*. Mumbai: FAC, 11 July-01 August 1999. p.20.
---. *Early works*. Mumbai: FAC, 07 – 29 January 2000. p.30.
---. *Erotica*. Mumbai: FAC, 02 – 30 December 2000. p.42.
---. *Excerpts from My Diary Pages*. Mumbai: FAC, 29 June – 20 July 2001. p.16.
Fine Art Resource. *Water Mark: The Water Colour show*. Mumbai: JAG, 02 – 11 December 1999. p.82.
Fine Art Resource. *A Global View: Indian Artists at Home in the World. Cu. by Bernhard Steinrucke*. Mumbai: JAG, 20 – 26 November 2000. p.56.
---. *Contemporary Miniatures: India and Pakistan*. Berlin: TFRS, 10 April-30 June 2003. p.20.
---. *Anticipations*. Mumbai: JAG, 08 – 14 December 2004. p.206.

Galerie 88. *Gulam Rasool Santosh*. Calcutta, 1991.
---. *J Sultan Ali*. Calcutta, 1991. p.22.
---. *Exhibition of Painting*. Calcutta: SAG, 10 – 16 December 1992; Bombay: JAG, 18 – 25 December 1992. p.20.
---. *Antaid: An Exhibition Of Paintings and Sculptures*. Calcutta: Galerie 88, 22 – 25 April 1993. p.38.
---. *Exhibition of Paintings*. Calcutta: Galerie 88, 16 – 30 June 1995. p.16.
---. *Reflections. Text by Arun Ghose*. Bombay: JAG, 17 – 23 October 1994. p.28.
---. *Perspecta: Paintings, Graphics and Sculptures*. Calcutta: Galerie 88, 23 – 25 August 1996. p.38.
Galerie Martini. *Indian Spring: Contemporary Women Artists*. New Delhi: GM, 31 March-01 May 1998. p.14.
Galerie Mirchandani + Steinruecke. *Artist Lives and Works in Baroda, Bombay, Calcutta, Mysore, Rotterdam, Trivandrum*. Mumbai: GMS, 10-28 August 2005. p.60.
Galerie Romain Rolland. *Ram Kumar. Text by Aman Nath*. New Delhi: GRR, 1988. p.24.
Galerie Romain Rolland. *Drawings 1996*. New Delhi: GRR, 16-29 February 1996. p.20.
Gallerie Ganesha. *10th Anniversary*. New Delhi: EHIHC, 22-29 October 1999; New Delhi: GG, 22 October-10 November 1999. p.36.
---. *12th Anniversary*. New Delhi: VAG, 16-22 November 2001. p.42.
---. *Nayika*. New Delhi: Shridharani Gallery, 28 October–06 November 2002. p.36.
---. *Shadanga*. New Delhi: VAG, 15-22 December 2004. p.42.
---. *Functional Art: Form Function and Fantasy*. New Delhi: VAG, 22-28 February 2006. p.44.
Gallery (The). *Indian Encounters: A Selection of Indian Contemporary Paintings*. Madras: TG, ---. p.20.
---. *With in the Frame: Contemporary Indian Painting in Miniature Format*. Madras: TG, ---. p.15.
Gallery 7. *Group Exhibition: Pushpamala N, Atul Dodiya, Vasudevan*. Mumbai: G7, 1985. p.8.
---. *Select Collection-1*. Mumbai: G7, 29 April-12 May 2004. p.16.
Gallery Art Motif. *Images on Paper*. New Delhi: GAM, 05-25 April 1996. p.20.
---. *Pastel. Cu. by Prayag Shukla*. New Delhi:GAM, 1996. p.28.
---. *Still Life: The Inscrutable Genre*. New Delhi: GAM, 2005. p.41.
Gallery Chemould. *Ram Kumar. Text by Shamlal*. Bombay: GC, 1966. p.22.
---. *Sultan Ali*. Bombay: GC, 1967. p.16.
---. *Ram Kumar*. Bombay: GC, 1969. p.32.
---. *Ram Kumar*. Bombay: GC, 1974. p.14.
---. *Indian Painters 1970 Tehran*. Mumbai: GC, 1970. p.14.
---. *Watercolours: A Broader Spectrum–I*. Mumbai: GC, 05-22 April 1995. p.16.
---. *Once Upon a Time and a Story was Born*. Mumbai: GC, 2000. p.20.
Gallery Espace. *Exhibition of Paintings by M.F. Husain and Contemporary Indian Artists*. New Delhi: GE, 17-18 April 1993. p.24.
---. *Bronze: Celebrating Centenary Year of Ram Kinkar Baij*. New Delhi: LKA, 28 November-12 December 2006. p.110.
---. *I Fear I Believe I Desire*. New Delhi: GE, 19 March-05 April 2007. p.50.
Gallery G. *Hues of Bengal*. Kolkata: GG, 17-23 February 2008. p.10.
Gallery Kanishka's. *Black and White*. Kolkata: GK, 15 February-10 March 2007. p.16.
---. *Roots in Hue: An Exhibition of Fine Art by Contemporary Artists*. Mumbai: JAG, 29 December 2005-04 January 2006. p.70.
---. *Evening in Paris, London, Pompeli, Florence, Rome, Venice*. Kolkata: GS, 05-28 October 2007. p.24.
---. *Gallery Sanskriti: Seventeenth Anniversary Show*. Kolkata: GS, 24 August-08 September 2007. p.20.
Gedung Pameran Senirupa. *Contemporary Art: Catalogue of the Non Aligned Countries 1995*. Indonesia: GPS, 28 April-30 June 1995. p.113.
Glenbarra (Japan). *Contemporary Indian Art: Glenbarra Art Museum Collection. Ed by Masanori Fukuoka*. Jihoji Hemeji (Japan): GJ, 1993. p.46.
---. Jogen Chowdhury: Enigmatic Visions works from the Art. Japan: GAM, 2005. p.26.
Grey Art Gallery. *Contemporary Indian Art: From The Chester And Davida Herwitz Family Collection. Text by Gieve Patel*. New York: GAG, 10 December 1985 – 25 May 1986. p.88.
Grosvenor Gallery. *Souza and Friends: Paintings and Drawings From the Masters of Indian Modernism*. London: GG, 03-27 September 2002. p.16.
Guild (The). ---. *K Laxma Goud*. Mumbai: Guild, 2003. p.18.

HEART. *Intuitive-Logic: A Festival of Indian Contemporary Painting*. New Delhi: HEART in Association with Mapin: Ahmedabad, 1997. (Exhibition:1 March–19 April 1997, in collaboration with NGMA, New Delhi and Bombay; Roopankar Museum of Fine Arts, Bharat Bhavan, Bhopal; British Council, Mumbai; Centre Art Gallery, Calcutta; Chitrakoot Art Gallery, Mumbai; Gallery Chemould and Max Mueller Bhavan, Mumbai; Prithvi Gallery and Pundole Art Gallery, Mumbai).
Hunter Museum of Art. *Husain: From the Collection of Chester and Davida Herwitz*. Chattanooga–Tennessee: HMA, 1988. p.14.

Institute of Contemporary Indian Art. *Young Guns*. Mumbai: ICIA, 2007. p.60.
---. *Cool School*. Mumbai: ICIA, 17 – 24 September 2008. p.4.
International Institute of Fine Arts. *Imprints: Indiart Show - Celebrating the India-Japan Friendship Year 2007*. Tokyo: Ueno Royal Museum, 2007. p.158.

Jamaat. *Jamaat*. Mumbai: Jamaat, 05 May-09 June 2001. p.21.
Jehangir Art Gallery. *Places For People*. Mumbai: JAG, 09-15 November; New Delhi: Ravindra Bhavan, 21 November-03 December 1981. p.24.
---. *Indian Print Making Today–1985*. Mumbai: JAG, 1985. p.10.
---. *Art For Cry*. Mumbai: JAG, 30 January-05 February; New Delhi: LKA, 17-23 February 1995. p.120.
---. *50th Aesthetic Stimulus. Cu. by Sangeeta Juneja*. Jaipur: JAG, 15 – 30 January 2007. p.40.

Kala Yatra. *Ram Kumar*. Bangalore: KA, 1988.
Kumar Gallery. *J Sultan Ali*, New Delhi: KG, 1963. p.16.
---. *Recent Paintings of Sultan Ali. Text by Sulochana Singh*. New Delhi: KG, 1964. p.14.
---. *J Sultan Ali 1969*. New Delhi: KG, 1969. p.26.

L.T.G. Art Gallery. *G R Santosh. Text: Hilal Ahmed and Shabir Santosh.* New Delhi: LTG, 2001. p.26.
Lalit Kala Akademi. *National Exhibition of Art 1960.* New Delhi: LKA, 30 March 1960. p.35.
---. *National Exhibition of Art: An Exhibition of Paintings, Sculptures, Graphics.* New Delhi: LKA, 05-08 February1964. p.410.
---. *Third Triennale India.* New Delhi: LKA, 03-05 February 1975. p.125.
---. *Fourth Triennale - India.* New Delhi: LKA,1978. p.120.
---. *Pictorial Space: A Point of View on Contemporary Indian Art. Com. by Geeta Kapur.* New Delhi: LKA–Rabindra Bhavan Galleries, 14 December 1977–3 January, 1978. p.40.
---. *25th National Exhibition of Art.* New Delhi: LKA, 20-24 February 1982. p.30.
---. *Fifth Triennale - India 1982.* New Delhi: LKA, 1982. p.102.
---. *Kala Mela.* New Delhi: LKA, 16 March-03 April 1982. p.46.
---. *Graphic Art in India since 1850. Com. Amit Mukhopadhyay And Others.* New Delhi: LKA, 1985. p.222.
---. *Award Winners National Exhibition of Art 1955–1990. Ed. by Amit Mukhopadhyaya.* New Delhi: LKA, 1990.
---. *Veteran Artists of India: An Exhibition of Painting, Graphics and Sculptures.* Bhubaneshwar: RLKK, 12 December 1990; Bangalore: KCP, 02-12 January 1991. p.56.
---.Catalogue 1: Collection from Lalit Kala Akademi 1958-1966. Ed. by *Amit Mukhopadhyay.* New Delhi: LKA, 1995. p.99.
---. *Major Trends in Indian Art. Cu. by R M Palaniapan.* New Delhi: LKA 25 September 12 October, 1997. p.86.
---. *40th National Exhibition of Contemporary Art 1997 Bangalore.* New Delhi: LKA, 1997. p.100.
---. *Ninth Triennale India–1997.* New Delhi: LKA, 03-31 December 1997. p.246.
---. *Lalit kala ratnas.* New Delhi: LKA, 09 August 2004. p.20.
---. *Resonance. Cu. By K T Ravindran.* New Delhi: LKA, 2005. p.192.
Lalit Kala Galleries. *Group Exhibition–1974. Text by Geeta Kapur.* New Delhi: Rabindra Bhavan Galleries, 1975. p.46.
---. *Indian Eclectics: Some New Sensibilities in Contemporary Art.* New Delhi: Rabindra Bhavan, 5–13 October, 1989. p.52.

Marvel Art Gallery. *Marvelous Show.* Ahmedabad: MAG, 2007. p.106.
Max Muller Bhavan. *Contemporary Paintings on War and Peace: An Exhibition of the Works of the Indo-German Artists.* Calcutta: MMB, 17-27 May 1990. p.22.
Mon Art Gallery. *Un Reve..... A Dream: A Collection of Work by 35 Well–Known Artists. Text by Bhavna Kakar.* Kolkata: Regency, 23 – 30 November, 2006. p.32.
Multiple Sclerosis Society of India. *Multiple Images.* Mumbai: MSSI, 05-11 January 1999. p.52.

National Gallery of Modern Art. *Handbook of Paintings and Graphics.* New Delhi: NGMA, 1974. p.30.
---. *Handbook of Bengal School.* New Delhi: NGMA, 1975. p.30.
---. *Jamini Roy 1887–1972: Centenary Exhibition.* New Delhi: NGMA, 1987. p.24.
---. *National Exposition of Contemporary Art–1991. Text by P N Mago.* New Delhi: NGMA, 1991. p.108.
---. *Young: Contemporary Artists From SAARC Countries.* Trivendrum: KKP, 12-18 October 1992; New Delhi: NGMA, 23 October-06 November 1992. p.44.
---. *State of the Art: An Exhibition of Computer-Aided Mixed-Media Paintings on Canvas.* New Delhi: NGMA, 1993. p.30.
---. *Indian Contemporary Art: An Exhibition from the Collection of the NGMA.* Kuala Lumpur: Galeri Petronas– Menara Dayabumi, August, 1995. p.56.
---. *Man and Nature: Reflections of Six Artists.* New Delhi: NGMA, 1995. p.24.
---. *Shilpayan. Designed by Latika Katt.* New Delhi: NGMA, 1996. p.48.
---. *Moderns: Inaugural Show.* Mumbai: NGMA, 1996. p.59.
---. *Shilpayan. Cu. by Latika Katt.* New Delhi: NGMA, 1996. p.96.
---. *Indian Contemporary Art.* Durban: Durban Art Gallery, 03-29 June; Johannesburg: Standard Bang Gallery, 07-20 July 1997. p.22
---. Santiniketan: *The Making of a Contextual Modernism (Rabindranath Tagore, Nandalal Bose, Benodebehari Mukherjee, Ramkinkar Baji). Cu by R Siva Kumar.* New Delhi: NGMA. 1997. p.46.
---. *Santiniketan: The Making of a Contextual Modernism. Int. by K G Subramanyan and Cu. by R Sivakumar.* New Delhi: NGMA.1997. p.127.
---. *Delhi Silpi Chakra: The Early Year.* New Delhi: NGMA, 04 December 1997-11 January 1998. p.60.
---. *Symbolism and Geometry in Indian Art.* New Delhi: NGMA, 14 February-22 March 1998. p.68.
---. *Wilberding Collection of Contemporary Indian Art.* Mumbai: NGMA, ---.June 1998. p.86.
---. *Dialogue: Interactions in Indian Art Part I - 1850 Onwards.* New Delhi: NGMA, 2001. p.30.
---. *Crossing Generation: Diverge.* New Delhi: NGMA, 02-14 December 2003. p.48.
---. *Pictorial Transformations: Treasures from the Collection of NGMA. Cu by Rajeev Lochan.* New Delhi: NGMA, 2003. p.40
---. *Selections from the Collection of the National Gallery of Modern Art.* New Delhi: NGMA, ---. p.24.
National Museum. *Restoration of Oil Painting: Techniques.* New Delhi: NM, ---. p.20.
Nitanjali Art Galleries. *Uninterupted Journies. Cu. by Elizabeth Rogers.* Mumbai: NAG, 3–27 March 2007. p.22.

Palette Art Gallery. *Red.* New Delhi: PAG, 20 February-06 March 2004. p.24.
---. *Palette 2005 - Part I.* New Delhi: PAG, 14-22 November 2005. p.40.
---. *Masters of Indian Contemporary Art. Cu. by Gayatri Sinha.* New Delhi: PAG, 2005.
---. *Roop Adhyatma.* New Delhi: PAG, 11 February-04 March 2006. p.32.
---. *Palette 2006-2007.* New Delhi: PAG, 31 January-07 February 2007. p.50.
Paul Robeson Gallery. *Post - Independence Contemporary Indian Art: Selection From the Sunanda and Umesh Gaur Collection.* New Jersey: PRG, 02 December 2002 – 14 March 2003. p.12.
Peabody Essex Museum. *Timeless Visions: Contemporary Art of India: From the Chester and Davida Herwitz Collection. Text by Susan S Bean.* Massachusetts: PEM, ---
---. *Gateway Bombay.* Salem Massachusetts: PEM, 14 July 2007-07 December 2008. p.66.
Point of View Art Gallery. *Southwards.* Mumbai: PVAG, 16-30 January 2008. p.12.
---. *Of Palettes and Chisels: Glimpses Of Contemporary Art of Bengal. Cu. by Usha Agarwal.* Mumbai: PVAG, 28 March – 11 April 2007. p.30.
Prakrit Arts. *Conglomeration: Indian Contemporary Artists 2007.* Chennai: PA, 2007. p.55.
Priyasri Art Gallery. *Postvisual World.* Mumbai: PAG, 25 February-15 March 2008. p.40.
Priyasri Patodia. *Drawing An Act of Art.* Mumbai: PP, 21 May-21 June 2005. p.20.
Pundole Art Gallery. *Ram Kumar.* Bombay: PAG, 1992. p.16.
---. *Mithuna: An Exhibition of Modern Indian Painting. Text by Narendra Panjwani.* Mumbai: PAG, 20 – 28 October 1995. p.20.
---. *Ram Kumar. Text by Ranjit Hoskote.* Bombay: PAG, 1996. p.14.

Rabi Art Gallery. *Collections.* Kolkata: Academy of Fine Arts, 28 April-04 May 2007. p.48.
Reliance Industries Limited. *Harmony show.* Mumbai: Nehru Centre, 02-08 April 1996. p.190.

---. *Harmony show: A Tribute to Art*. Mumbai: Nehru Centre, 03-09 March 1998. p.62.
---. *Harmony Show: A Tribute to Art*. Mumbai: Nehru Centre, 03-10 April 1999. p.58.
---. *6th Harmony Show 2001: A Tribute to Art*. Mumbai: Nehru Centre, 08-15 April 2001. p.74.
---. *7th Harmony show 2002*. Mumbai: Nehru Centre, 06-14 April 2002. p.68.
---. *8th Harmony Show-2003*. Mumbai: Nehru Centre, 04-13 April 2003. p.68.
---. *9th Harmony Show-2006: A Tribute to Art*.Mumbai: Nehru Centre, 02-11 April 2006. p.81.
Romain Rolland Galerie. *Jamini Roy and His Roots. Text by: Suneet Chopra*. New Delhi: RRG, 1995. p.18.
Royal Academy of Arts. *Contemporary Indian Art: An Exhibition of the Festival of India–1982*. London: Burlington House, *the Gesture and Motif*, 18 September–5 October; *Stories and Situations* 9–31 October, 1982. London: Indian Advisory Committee, Festival of India (U.K.). 1982. p.46.
RPG Enterprises. *Bombay*. ---: RPGE, ---. p.60.

Safdar Hashmi Memorial Trust. *Artists Alert*. New Delhi: Rabindra Bhavan, 12-15 April 1989. p.128.
Saffronart. *Generation*. Mumbai: Saffronart, 04-31 March 2004. p.40.
Sakshi Gallery. *Creative Space: Exhibition of Paintings and Sculptures*. New Delhi: VAG, 23-29 November 2002. p.30.
---. *M F Husain: Serigraphs and Reproductions*. Mumbai: SG, 2002. p.18.
---. *Making of Divinity*. Mumbai: SG, 20 May-30 June 2006. p.36.
Sanskriti Pratishthan. *Indian Eclectics : Some New Sensibilities in Contemporary Art*. New Delhi: LKG, 05-13 October 1989. p.2.
Sarala Art Centre. *Maqbool Fida Husain*. Madras: SAC, 1975.
Sarjan Art Gallery. *Window to Vistas: Paradise to Landscapes Cu.by Renowned Artists. Text by Ratan Parimoo*. Vadodara: SAG, 4–18 March, 2001. p.28.
---. *Reflection*. Vadodara: SAG, 24-28 February 2003. p.20.
---. *Reflection. Cu. by M Balamani*. Vadodara, SAG, 24–28 February, 2006. p.38.
---. *Santiniketan Show. Text by R Siva Kumar*. Vadodara, SAG, 17–27 January, 2006.p.24.
Singapore Art Museum. *From the Everyday to the Imagined: An Exhibition of Indian Art. Cu. by Jean Wee*. Singapore: SAM, 17 November 2007 – 16 January 2008; Singapore: MA, 14 February – 25 April 2008. p.76.
---. *Cubism In Asia: Unbounded Dialogues*. Tokyo: NMMA, 09 August – 02 October 2005; Korea: NMCA, 11 November 2005 – 30 January 2006; Singapore: SAM, 18 February – 09 April 2006. p.276.
State of the Art. *State of the Art: An Exhibition of Electronically - Aided Canvases*. Bombay: SA, 1991. p.30.
Surendra Paul Art Gallery. *Probing Eye: 38 Insightful Photographic Impressions by Nineteen Distinguished Painters and Sculptors*. New Delhi: SPAG, 25 October-15 November 1998. p.24.

Takaoka Municipal Museum of Art. *Indian Contemporary Art*. Tokyo: TMMA, 1998. p.56.
Tangerine Art Space. *Pulsating Rhythms on Paper*. Bangalore: TAS, 1-26 September 2007. p.36.
---. *Abstract Visions: Parallel Perceptions*. Bangalore: TAS, 21-22 May 2007. p.58.
Tao Art Gallery. *Sacred Space*. Mumbai: TAG, 28 January-21 February 2000. p.10.
TAO Art Gallery. *Shantipath: An Exhibition For World Peace: At the End of the War Who is the Winner? Cu. by Kalapana Shah and Himanshu Desai*. Mumbai: TAO, 2003. p.26.
---. *Illumination: Paintings, Poems*. Mumbai: TAO, 26 February 20 - March, 2004. p.42.
---. *Faces*. Mumbai: TAG, 17 – 25 October 2008. p.2.
Tao Contemporary Art Gallery. *Sacred Space*. Mumbai: TCAG, 28 January-21 February 2000. p.8.
---. *Quotable Stencil: Contemporary Painting and Graphics with Photographic Reference*. Mumbai: TCAG, 2002. p.20.
---. *Shantipath: An Exhibition for World Peace*. Mumbai: TCAG, 2003. p.46.
---. *Illumination: Paintings, Poems*. Mumbai: TCAG, 26 February-20 March 2004. p.24.
---. *Tao of Shiva: The Lord of Light*. Mumbai: TCAG, 2004. p.40.
---. *BW: An Expression in Black and White*. Mumbai: TCAG, 2006. p.82.
---. *Evam*. Mumbai: TCAG, 20-24 January 2006. p.110.

ULTIMA. *Art Contemporary Indian Masters*. Bangalore: Hourglass Essentials, 2006. p.44.
Uttarayan. *New Mediatic Realism*. Baroda: Uttarayan, ---. p.40.

Vadehra Art Gallery. *Masters: Best of Some Outstanding Delhi Artists*. New Delhi: VAG, 01 – 07 October 1991. p.30.
---. *Ram Kumar*. New Delhi: VAG, 1992. p.34.
---. *Ram Kumar: Recent Paintings*. New Delhi: VAG, 1993. p.36.
---. *Reflections and images*. New Delhi: VAG, 06 – 21 August 1993. p.30.
---. *Jogen Chowdhury Drawings 1959–1994*. New Delhi: VAG, ---
---. *Recent Trends in Contemporary Indian art*. New Delhi: VAG, 01 August – 07 September 1995. p.32.
---. *Tyeb Mehta Paintings. Text by Kamla Ganesh*. New Delhi: VAG, 1998. p.12.
---. *Ram Kumar Recent Works*. New Delhi: VAG, 2000. p.09.
---. *Real in Realism*. New Delhi: VAG, 08 – 28 October 2002. p.24.
---. *Ram Kumar*. New Delhi: VAG, 2003. p.15.
---. Sacred Feminine. Madras: VFA, 2005; Madras: AG, 2005. p.64.
Village Gallery. *Ganesh Pyne: Jottings–Preliminary Drawings for Paintings*. New Delhi: VG, 1990. p.12.
---. *Ganesh Pyne: Jottings in Mixed Media*. New Delhi: VG, 1996. p.18.
---. *Ganesh Pyne: Water Colours*. New Delhi, 20 December 2003–20 February, 2004. p.24.
Visual Art. *Evolution: A Glimpse of Contemporary Art by Kolkata Artists*. London: VA, 08-14 October 2006. p.40.
Vivid Hues. *Vivid Hues*. Mumbai: VH, 09-13 April 2008. p.14.
Whiteleys Art Gallery (London). *Chamatkara: Myth and Magic in Indian Art. Cu. by Rakhi Sarkar*. London: WAG, 29 October–15 November 1996. p.28. (See also CIMA).

Window (The). *Window is Open*. Mumbai: TW, 01 October 1998–1999. p.28.
Willem Baars Project. *Everything*. ---: WBP, 08 November – 06 December 2008. p.2.

Auction Catalogues

Apparaoart

Bengal Art Auction: Early and Current Art of the Region. 03.09.2006.
Specially South.29.07.2007.
Bengal Art Auction II: Early and Current Art of the Region. 18.11.2007.
Women Inspired: Contemporary Indian Art by and of Women. 18.04.2008.
Specially South Sculptures: Contemporary Sculptures of South India. 20.04.2008.

Asta Guru

Contemporary Indian Art: Online Auction. 22.02.2008.
Modern and Contemporary Indian Art: Online Auction. 21.08.2008.

Bloomsbury

Modern and Contemporary British Art. London. 22.11.2006.

Bonham's

Modern and Contemporary Indian Paintings. London. 16.06.1999.
Modern and Contemporary Paintings from the Indian Sub-Continent. London. 14.07.2000.
Modern and Contemporary Paintings from the Indian Sub-Continent. London. 31.10.2000.
Modern and Contemporary Paintings from the Indian Sub-Continent. London. 12.06.2001.
Islamic and Indian Art. Knightsbridge. 17.10.2002.
Indian and Islamic Art. London. 01.05.2003.
Islamic and Indian Art. London. 28.04.2005.
Islamic and Indian Art. London. 13.10.2005.
Islamic and Indian Art Part II. London. 06.04.2006.
Works on Paper by Francis Newton Souza. London. 03.05.2006.
Contemporary Indian and Pakistani Paintings. London. 14.09.2006.
Modern and Contemporary Indian and Pakistani Paintings. London. 21.05.2007.
Islamic and Indian Art: Part II Indian Art Including Modern and Contemporary Indian and Pakistani Paintings. London. 25.10.2007.
Modern and Contemporary Arab, Iranian, Indian and Pakistani Art. Dubai. 03.03.2008.
Islamic and Indian Art: Part II Indian Art Including Contemporary Indian and Pakistani Paintings. London. 06.10.2008.

Bowring's

Paintings and Works of Art. New Delhi. 05.11.2001.
Modern and Contemporary Indian Paintings. Mumbai. 21.03.2002.
European, Modern and Contemporary Indian Paintings. New Delhi. 20.11.2002.
House Contents including Furniture and Works of Art. Bangalore. 12.12.2002.
Furniture, Works of Art, Paintings, Carpets and Clocks. Kolkata. 17.01.2003.

Christie's

Contemporary Indian Art. Mumbai. 20.12.1987.
Indian Contemporary Paintings. London. 16.10.1995.
Islamic Art and Indian Miniatures and Rugs and Carpets. London. 25.04.1996.
Islamic Art and Indian Miniatures and Rugs and Carpets. London. 15.10.1996.
Indian Contemporary Art. London. 04.06.1997.
Twentieth Century Indian Art. London. 02.06.1998.
Twentieth Century Indian Art. London. 05.10.1999.
Indian and Southeast Asian Art Including 20th Century Indian Paintings. New York. 20.09.2000.
Southeast Asian and 20th Century India Picture Sale. Singapore. 01.04.2001.
Indian and Southeast Asian Art Including 20th Century Indian Paintings. New York. 17.10.2001.
Islamic and Indian Works of Art. New York. 18.10.2001.
Southeast Asian and 20th Century Indian Pictures. Hong Kong. 28.04.2002.
Indian and Southeast Asian Art Including 20th Century Indian Paintings. New York. 19.09.2002.
Southeast Asian and 20th Century Indian Pictures. Hong Kong. 06.07.2003.
Indian and Southeast Asian Art Including 20th Century Indian Paintings. New York. 17.09.2003.
Indian and Islamic Works of Art. South Kensington. 17.10.2003.
Indian and Southeast Asian Art Including 20th Century Indian Paintings. New York. 25.03.2004.
Southeast Asian and 20th Century Indian Pictures. Hong Kong. 25.04.2004.
Indian and Southeast Asian Art Including 20th Century Indian Paintings. New York. 23.09.2004.
Indian and Islamic Art Including 20th Century Indian and Middle Eastern Paintings. South Kensington. 15.10.2004.
Indian and Southeast Asian Art Including Modern Indian Paintings. New York. 31.03.2005.
Southeast Asian and Modern Indian Paintings Including Contemporary Art. Hong Kong. 29.05.2005.
Indian and Southeast Asian Art Including Modern and Contemporary Indian Art. New York. 21.09.2005.
Modern and Contemporary Indian Art. New York. 30.03.2006.
International Modern and Contemporary Art. Dubai. 24.05.2006.
Modern and Contemporary Indian Art. New York. 20.09.2006.
International Modern and Contemporary Art. Dubai. 01.02.2007.
Modern and Contemporary Indian Art. New York. 21.03.2007.
Modern and Contemporary Indian Art. New York. 21.05.2007.
South Asian Modern + Contemporary Art. New York. 20.09.2007.
South Asian Modern + Contemporary Art, Part I & II. New York. 20.03.2008.
Scholar's Vision: The Family Collection. New York. 20.03.2008.
South Asian Modern + Contemporary Art. London. 11.06.2008.
South Asian Modern + Contemporary Art. London. 16.09.2008.
Asian Contemporary Art. Hong Kong. 30.11.2008.
Asian Contemporary Art, Part I & II. Hong Kong. 01.12.2008.
South Asian Modern + Contemporary Art. New York. 19.03.2009

Emamichisel

Indian Modern and Contemporary Art, Part I & II. 23.02.2008.
Contemporary and Modern Art. 18.11.2008.

HEART

Intuitive-Logic II. New Delhi. 15.11.1997.
Intuitive-Logic: The Next Step. New Delhi. 28.11.1999.
(Auctions curated by Neville Tuli.).

Larasati

Picturing of Asia Fine Art Auction: Modern and Contemporary Art. Singapore. 13.04.2008.

Osian's

India: the Passionate Detachment: Curated Auctions of Indian Modern and Contemporary Art and Books. Mumbai. 23.02.2001.
India: A Historical Lila Auctions of Indian Modern and Contemporary Paintings, Drawings, and Graphic Art. Mumbai. 19.10.2001.
India: A Historical Mela the ABC of India the Art, Book and Cinema. Mumbai. 18.03.2002.
India: A Historical Epic India in the Making 1757–1950 from Surrender to Revolt Swaraj to Responsibility. Mumbai. 14.08.2002.
Masterpieces and Museum-Quality Indian Modern and Contemporary Paintings. Mumbai. 05.12.2002.

Forty Masterpieces: 20th Century Painting and Drawing from India, Pakistan, Bangladesh and Sri Lanka. Mumbai. 27.03.2003.
Figurative Non-Figurative Narration: Auctions of Indian Modern and Contemporary Paintings and Books. Mumbai. 27.11.2003.
Masterpieces and Museum-Quality III: Indian Contemporary Paintings with Rare Books and Vintage Film Memorabilia. Mumbai. 26.03.2004.
Masterpieces and Museum Quality Series: Indian Contemporary Art Books, Paintings and Sculpture. New Delhi. 15.10.2004.
Indian Contemporary Art, Paintings, Drawings and Sculpture. Mumbai. 09.02.2005.
Masterpieces and Museum Quality Series: Indian Contemporary Art. Mumbai. 02.12.2005.
Masterpieces and Museum Quality Series VI. New Delhi. 01.03.2006.
ABC Series The Art, Book and Cinema. New Delhi. 20.07.2006.
Forty Masterpieces: The Masterpieces and Museum Quality Series. Mumbai 09.09.2006.
Historical Series III. New Delhi. 24.11.2006.
Masterpieces and Museum-Quality Series. Mumbai. 31.01.2007.
ABC Series III: The Art, Book and Cinema. New Delhi. 29.03.2007.
Masterpieces and ABC Series Includes Indian Modern and Contemporary Art, Books, Popular Culture and Pakistani Film Posters. New Delhi. 27.07.2007.
Masters Series. Mumbai. 08.09.2007.
Indian Modern and Contemporary Art: 100 Years of Wonder. Mumbai. 19.01.2008.
Indian Modern and Contemporary Art. New Delhi. 18.03.2008.
ABC Series IV: The Art, Book and Cinema. New Delhi. 15.07.2008.
Indian Modern and Contemporary Art & Craft. Mumbai. 27.11.2008.
ABC Series V: The Art, Book and Cinema. Jaipur. 23.01.2009.
Indian Modern and Contemporary Art. New Delhi. 21.02.2009.
Indian Modern and Contemporary Art & Craft. Mumbai. 23.03.2009.

(All auctions curated by Neville Tuli.).

Philips
Contemporary Art. London. 13.02.2009.

Saffronart
Indian Contemporary Art. 01.12.2000.
Indian Contemporary Art. 22.03.2001.
Modern Indian Art. 16.05.2001.
Indian Contemporary Fine Art. 21.09.2001.
Indian Contemporary Art. 06.12.2001.
Modern Indian Paintings. 16.05.2002.
Aspects of Modern Indian Paintings. 01.10.2002.
Online Auction. 04.12.2002.
Modern Indian Painting. 08.05.2003.
Modern Indian Paintings. 04.12.2003.
Modern Indian Paintings. 06.05.2004.
Modern Indian Paintings. 02.12.2004.
Modern and Contemporary Paintings. 02.03.2005.
Modern and Contemporary Indian Art. 12.05.2005.
Modern and Contemporary Indian Art. 08.12.2005.
Contemporary. 16.03.2006.
Modern Indian Art. 11.05.2006.
Contemporary. 07.09.2006.
Modern Indian Art. 07.12.2006.
Contemporary. 08.03.2007.
Modern Indian Art. 07.06.2007.
Contemporary. 06.09.2007.
Modern Indian Art. 06.12.2007.
Contemporary. 13.03.2008.
Modern and Contemporary Indian Art. 19.06.2008.
Contemporary. 04.09.2008.
Modern and Contemporary Indian Art. 11.12.2008.
Modern and Contemporary Indian Art. 12.03.2009

Sotheby's
Timeless Art. Mumbai. 26.03.1989.
Indian, European Oriental Paintings and Works of Art. New Delhi. 09.10.1992.
Contemporary Indian Paintings. New York. 12.06.1995.
Contemporary Indian Paintings Part II. New York. 03.04.1996.
Islamic and Indian Art. London. 25.04.1996.
Indian and Southeast Asian Art. New York. 19.09.1996.
Modern and Indian Contemporary Paintings. London. 08.10.1996.
Indian Sale. London. 08.05.1997.
Modern and Indian Contemporary Paintings. New York. 10.10.1997.
Indian and Southeast Asian Art. New York. 16.09.1998.
Indian Miniatures the Travel Sale: India and the Far East Modern and Contemporary South Asian Paintings. London. 17.06.1999.
Indian and Southeast Asian Art. New York. 16.09.1999.
Indian Southeast Asian Art. New York. 23.03.2000.
Indian Miniatures the Travel Sale: India and the Far East Modern and Contemporary South Asian Paintings. London. 08.06.2000.
Indian and Southeast Asian Art. New York. 22.09.2000.
Contemporary Indian Paintings. New York. 05.12.2000.
Indian and Southeast Asian Art. New York. 20.03.2001.
Indian and Southeast Asian Art. New York. 21.09.2001.
Indian and Southeast Asian Art. New York. 24.03.2004.
Indian and Southeast Asian Art Including Modern Indian Paintings. New York. 24.09.2004.
Indian and Southeast Asian Art Including Modern Indian Paintings. New York. 01.04.2005.
20th Century Asian Art. London. 14.07.2005.
Indian and Southeast Asian Art Including Modern Indian Paintings From the Wilberding Collection. 20.09.2005.
Indian and Southeast Asian Art. New York. 29.03.2006.
Indian Sale. London. 23.05.2006.
Indian Art: Including Miniatures and Modern Paintings. New York. 19.09.2006.
Indian and Southeast Asian Art. New York. 19.09.2006.
Indian Contemporary Art. New York. 22.09.2006.
Indian Art: Including Miniatures and Modern Paintings. New York. 22.03.2007.
Indian Sale. London. 24.05.2007.
Indian Art. New York. 17.07.2007.
Indian Art: Including Modern Painting and Miniatures. New York. 19.09.2007.
Contemporary Art South Asia, Indian, Pakistan. New York. 21.09.2007
Indian Art. New York. 19.03.2008.
Indian Art. New York. 02.05.2008.
Contemporary Art: Evening Auction. London. 01.07.2008.
Contemporary Art: Afternoon Auction. London. 02.07.2008.
Modern and Contemporary Art South Asia. New York. 18.09.2008.
Modern and Contemporary Asian Art: Evening Sale. Hon Kong. 04.10.2008.
Contemporary Art: Evening Auction. London. 17.10.2008.
Contemporary Art: Day Sale. London. 20.10.2008.
Contemporary Art: Evening Auction. London. 11.11.2008.
Contemporary Art: Afternoon Auction. London. 12.11.2008.
Contemporary Art: Day Auction. London. 06.02.2009.
Indian and Southeast Asian Art. New York. 18.03.2009
Contemporary Art. Doha. 18.03.2009

Triveda
Modern and Contemporary India Painting. New Delhi. 25.10.2006.
Modern and Contemporary India Art. New Delhi. 13.04.2007.
Indian Art: Early to Contemporary. New Delhi. 27.02.2008.

EXPLANATION OF CATALOGUING TERMS

Any statement of authorship, attribution, provenance, origin, date, age, and condition is a statement of opinion and is not to be taken as a statement of fact. Osian's reserves the right, in forming their opinion, to consult and rely upon any expert or authority considered by them to be reliable.

1. The term 'signed and dated' (S/d) and/or inscribed means that in our opinion the signature and/or date and/or inscription are from the hand of the artist.

   FORMAT for Auction Lot Caption is as follows:

   Lot Number
   Artist name
   [Date of Birth – Date of Death]
   Title
   Medium, Date
   Signature details
   Size in inches (in centimetres)
   Lower & Upper Price Estimates in Indian Rupees (INR)
   Lower & Upper Price Estimates in US Dollars (US $)

2. For all art works the dimensions are given height before width in inches (centimeters).

3. Osian's has tried to provide the best quality acid-free mounts to works wherever appropriate, and has reframed works wherever possible, from quality framers.

ABBREVIATIONS

AHJ	Art Heritage Journal
AIFACS	All India Fine Arts and Crafts Society, New Delhi
b.	Born
BAAC	Birla Academy of Art & Culure, Kolkata
BAS.	Bombay Art Society
b&w	Black & White
c.	circa
CIMA	Centre for International Modern Art, Kolkata
CUP	Cambridge University Press
Ed.	Editor
Eds.	Editors
Ex.	Exhibition
ExC	Exhibition Catalogue
ffp	Free Front Endpaper
For.	Forwarder
INTACH	Indian National Trust for Architectural Conservation & Heritage
Inted.	International Edition
JAG	Jehangir Art Gallery
LKA	Lalit Kala Akademi
LKC	Lalit Kala Contemporary
Mapin	Mapin Publishing Private Limited, Ahmedabad
NCPA	National Center for the Performing Arts, Mumbai
NGMA	National Gallery of Modern Art, New Delhi & Mumbai
OUP	Oxford University Press
p	Page
PAH	Previous Auction High
pp	Pages
rpt.	Reproduced
S/d	Signed & dated
Verso	reverse side
Comp.	Compiled
Cu.	Curator
c.c	centre centre
c.l.	centre left
c.r.	centre right
l.c.	lower centre
l.l.	lower left
l.r.	lower right
t.c.	top centre
t.l.	top left
t.r.	top right
Tr.	Translator

Lot Index By Artist

OSIAN's
Connoisseurs of Art

Select Masterpieces of
INDIAN MODERN & CONTEMPORARY ART

Date of Auction: TUESDAY, 30 JUNE 2009
THE TAJ MAHAL PALACE & TOWER, Apollo Bunder, Mumbai

TELEPHONE/WRITTEN BID FORM

To
OSIAN'S – CONNOISSEURS OF ART PVT. LTD.
G-2B Nariman Bhavan
Nariman Point
Mumbai 400 021. INDIA

Please bid on my behalf at the Auction, without any legal obligations of any kind on the part of OSIAN's for the following lot(s) upto the price(s) for each lot mentioned below. These bids are to be executed as cheaply as is permitted by other bids or reserves, if any. I agree to comply with and be bound by the terms and conditions of the Auction as printed in the Catalogue.

These bids shall be treated as offers made by me on the Terms and Conditions of the Auction printed in the Catalogue. I shall not hold OSIAN's responsible for failing to execute any or all of these bids. I agree without demur that bids of identical prices are received by OSIAN's, the first bid received by OSIAN's as decided by OSIAN's shall take precedence and that decisions taken by OSIAN's in respect of the Auction shall be final and binding on me.

Lot No.	Title or Description	Bid Price in INR Rs / US$ (Excluding Buyers Premium & Sales Tax)

Would you also like to bid on the Telephone? Yes ☐ No ☐ Tel. No. (1) ____________ (2) ____________

PLEASE USE BLOCK LETTERS

Full Name ____________
Address ____________
Tel No. ____________ Fax No. ____________
Email ____________

BANKERS DETAILS

Name ____________
Address ____________
Account No. ____________

PLEASE CHECK YOUR BID
Bids must be in numerical order of Lot Numbers as in the Catalogue.
Lot(s) purchased shall be released by OSIAN's only upon realisation of the Purchase Price for such Lot(s) in full.
Photocopies of the Bidding Slip duly signed by the Bidder will be accepted as legal offer.

Date Signature

Please courier all bids to the above address or fax to: +91 22 6632 5655

95